COMBAT AND SURVIVAL

WHAT IT TAKES TO FIGHT AND WIN

VOLUME
7

Originally published in the United Kingdom in weekly parts **COMBAT & SURVIVAL** is a study of the armed forces at work. It shows the skills taught to soldiers and the way in which military units operate. It examines the weapons and equipment used by different armies; and, by looking at recruit training and exercises, **COMBAT & SURVIVAL** demonstrates how the armed forces develop individual responsibility, leadership and initiative.

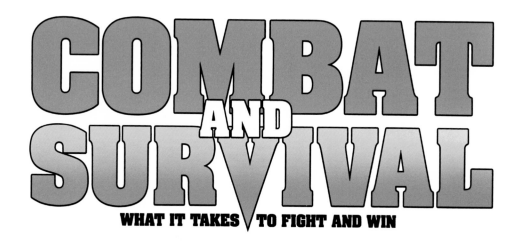

COMBAT AND SURVIVAL

WHAT IT TAKES TO FIGHT AND WIN

VOLUME
7

H. S. STUTTMAN, INC. *publishers*   Westport, Connecticut 06889

Contents

Volume 7

Published by H. S. STUTTMAN INC.
Westport, Connecticut 06889
© Aerospace Publishing 1991
ISBN 0-87475-560-3

1P(1632)30

SETTING AN AMBUSH

7 good ambush sites

1. **Routes known to be in regular use by enemy forces.**
2. **Admin areas and water points.**
3. **In counter-insurgency operations, the approaches to villages and suspected arms caches.**
4. **Places where the vegetation changes, e.g. the edge of a forest.**
5. **The enemy's line of retreat after a successful attack by friendly forces.**
6. **The approaches to your own defensive positions.**
7. **The withdrawal route from your own ambush (to catch pursuing enemy troops).**

The aftermath of a successful ambush: you emerge from cover to briefly check the enemy casualties before vanishing back into the trees. It is often thought that ambushing is only a counter-insurgency tactic, but it has enormous application in a conventional war.

One of the most difficult operations you can take part in is an ambush. But a properly planned and relentlessly executed ambush will pay you enormous dividends. Even the smallest combat team can inflict massive casualties on an enemy force far stronger than themselves. These basic principles are based on the British Army's methods of laying an ambush.

The ambush is perhaps best known as an extremely effective counter-insurgency technique, usually involving a patrol of platoon strength, following a carefully laid plan. But you can use the same techniques in conventional warfare, when the operation may involve anything from a section to an entire battalion. You might then find yourself as part of a fighting patrol whose task is to dominate No Man's Land, and setting an ambush for an enemy fighting patrol.

Deliberate and immediate

There are two categories of ambush: the deliberate, and the immediate. You would lay a deliberate ambush as a result of specific intelligence that the enemy will be using a particular route or meeting at a particular spot. It is a planned operation with a particular objective.

You would set an immediate ambush, on the other hand, on the spur of the moment, as a reaction to events on the battlefield or as a result of receiving 'hot' information.

If, for instance, you were with a fighting patrol and saw an enemy patrol approaching your position, your obvious course would be to mount an impromptu ambush at once. It's on occasions like this that your skill and training in ambush techniques will be most taxed – and most valuable.

Plan if you can

A deliberate ambush needs very careful planning. If possible, recce the site first. If you can't do this in person, use maps and photographs, and check your information once you arrive at the site.

In any ambush, you must lay your men out properly. If there is only one approach to the site, you can follow basic ambush drill. This means that

The work phase
After occupation, on a given signal work begins. While each group puts out sentries, the rest put out mines, ambush lights, trip flares, booby traps, Claymores and grenade necklaces; improve fields of fire and observation; dig in if necessary; and, finally, camouflage their positions. This must be done in complete silence and with minimum movement as this is the time when you are most vulnerable.

Ambush set
Once the work phase is over and everyone is in position, the ambush commander whispers into the ear of each man, 'Ambush set'. From then on it is safety catches off, no movement, and everyone looking at his arc of fire over his sights. The commander takes up his position in the middle of the killing group.

Ambush lights
These are a very useful ambush tool, usually knocked up by the unit out of car headlamps and 12-volt batteries. They illuminate the enemy while you remain in total darkness, but if the enemy are quick on the draw they may shoot them out: do not put them right next to you for that reason. Make sure that the soldier carrying them knows what he is doing, as switching them on prematurely is disastrous.

Communication
The system of information passage in the ambush position must be foolproof. Cut-off groups must be able to warn of enemy approach and indicate their strength to the ambush commander. Duplicate your means – radio, comms cord, field telephone – and make sure everything works.

you should be able to conceal yourselves effectively, in sufficient depth to absorb and overcome an enemy counter-attack, and with all possible approaches to your position covered.

If the enemy is likely to approach from more than one direction, you will need to set an area ambush. Essentially this is a set of mutually supporting basic ambushes, each with its own commander and arcs of fire.

You will need to make sure that each group knows where the others are, that their arcs of fire don't endanger any other group, and that com-

Spring the ambush
The best way to start the ball rolling is with several very large bangs, i.e. the Claymores or PAD mines.

CONDUCT OF THE AMBUSH

The aim is to do the damage in the first few seconds of the ambush. Everyone must put down very rapid fire as soon as the Claymore mines have gone off and keep firing, even if you run out of positive targets, until you get the signal for 'watch and shoot': either a whistle blast or voice.

1. Watch and shoot
Everyone momentarily stops firing and looks for movement of any type in the killing area, firing if they spot anything.
2. Cease fire
Use whistle and voice so that everyone gets the message.
3. Move out
Again, duplicate the signal to avoid confusion.

Rules for opening fire
These must be very carefully briefed. No-one should open fire until the chosen signal is given unless an individual is sure the enemy has seen him, in which case he may initiate the ambush by firing.

Longer-term ambushes can be conducted from a patrol base, but you have to be ready to move at all times. These would-be ambushers have been ambushed themselves while on exercise and must grab their kit and bug out as fast as they can.

munications between the groups and the ambush commander are foolproof.

Passing the time

Many ambushes are sprung within a few hours of your setting them. But if you are going to be on site for more than 12 hours you will need to set up a patrol base away from the site and organise a system of shifts, or reliefs, so that everyone has a chance to eat and sleep.

Set up your base as you would a patrol base, with a commander and sentries, far enough away from the ambush site to prevent the one drawing attention to the other. Make sure that you can withdraw at a moment's notice. Once you have sprung your ambush, you'll need to move out fast. The base will be your RV before finally leaving the area.

Depending on the number of men available, divide the patrol into at least two groups – one to be the ambush group, the other on relief. If

'Hammer and anvil'
Cover all potential escape routes from the killing zone with Claymores, AP mines and booby traps if you have time. Five-gallon drums with PE charges are particularly effective at covering a wide area; the resultant fireball from the vapourised fuel will also help to illuminate the target. These measures constitute the anvil on which the small-arms fire and Claymores of the killing group 'hammer' the enemy.

Low wire entanglement
Excellent strung between trees and pickets in long grass, it can be used both to strengthen your own ambush position against attack and to slow down the enemy trying to hot-foot it out of the killing zone. Careful siting is necessary so as not to compromise your position.

SECTION LINEAR AMBUSH

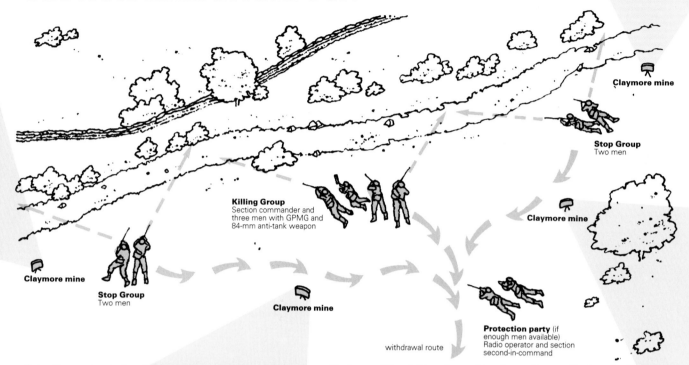

Claymore mine

Stop Group
Two men

Killing Group
Section commander and
three men with GPMG and
84-mm anti-tank weapon

Claymore mine

Claymore mine

Stop Group
Two men

Claymore mine

Protection party (if
enough men available)
Radio operator and section
second-in-command

withdrawal route

A section ambush should be arranged around a killing ground between 30 and 50 metres wide, depending on the terrain. Make sure the site does not have an easy escape route for enemy not hit in the initial burst of fire.

PLATOON 'T' BASIC AMBUSH

Your direction of approach

Claymore mines

Claymore mines

3 section

Platoon Sergeant & runner

light mortar

Claymore mines

2 section

1 section

Claymore mines

Killing Group

Platoon Commander & Radio operator

Killing Group

track

killing ground

*In a **Platoon 'T'** basic ambush two sections are used to form the killing group, with the third section forming a flank protection party in the rear. Use this along a very likely enemy approach route. The distance between men and groups depends on the ground and whether it is night or day.*

PLATOON TRIANGULAR AMBUSH

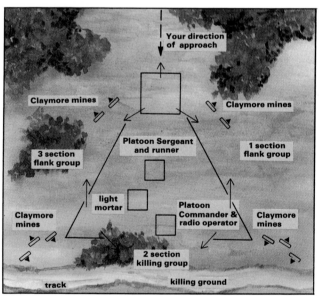

Your direction of approach

Claymore mines

Claymore mines

3 section flank group

Platoon Sergeant and runner

1 section flank group

light mortar

Claymore mines

Platoon Commander & radio operator

Claymore mines

2 section killing group

track

killing ground

*This is another form of basic ambush used when there is only one likely approach. The platoon is deployed for all-round defence in an area which gives good concealment. Where there are several approaches, each section can deploy into a separate ambush: this is called an **Area Ambush**.*

you can make up a third group, use it as a reserve.

Rotate each group one at a time. And make sure that the ambush group is relieved at pre-arranged times and that you warn them with pre-arranged signals when the relief group is on its way. Otherwise, they may simply be taken for the enemy and shot. For the same reason, don't send reliefs at night, when you should treat any movement as hostile.

Night and day

Unless you are fighting in jungle or some other heavily wooded or overgrown terrain, the chances are that you'll mount a short-term operation at night. In darkness your ambush group is more easily hidden not only before but during and after a firefight. On a night ambush, follow the following rules.

1 Shield any flares you use so that they light up the enemy on the killing ground but don't blind the ambush party.

2 Mark the left and right arcs of fire of each group and each individual with sticks in the ground. Otherwise you can become disorientated in the dark and may shoot at friendly troops.

3 Don't let anyone in the ambush group move at all. All movement at night is hostile. Men have been killed by their own mates from disregarding this rule.

At the sharp end

In your ambush party itself you will usually have several groups of men. One of these is the killing group, whose job it is to cover the killing ground and spring the ambush. They will have a high proportion of automatic weapons to bring maximum firepower onto the enemy.

In addition you will have flank groups – how many depends on the size of the patrol. They warn the killing group of the enemy's approach, and deal with any attempt he makes to escape the killing ground. They also contribute to the all-round defence and depth of the ambush party.

A successful ambush takes cunning, patience and enormous care. But it can bring you huge tactical advantages. The elements of surprise and concentrated fire let a small body of men take on a much larger force, and cause damage out of all proportion to the attackers' numbers. Knowing how to lay an effective ambush is one of the most valuable military skills you can learn.

PLATOON LINEAR AMBUSH

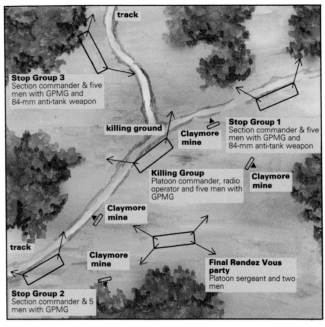

track

Stop Group 3
Section commander & five men with GPMG and 84-mm anti-tank weapon

killing ground

Stop Group 1
Section commander & five men with GPMG and 84-mm anti-tank weapon

Claymore mine

Killing Group
Platoon commander, radio operator and five men with GPMG

Claymore mine

Claymore mine

track

Claymore mine

Final Rendez Vous party
Platoon sergeant and two men

Stop Group 2
Section commander & 5 men with GPMG

In this platoon linear ambush, the stop groups warn the killing group of the enemy's approach, allowing the leading enemy element to pass through so that their main body enters the killing area. Obviously the exact layout of this ambush varies with terrain, and stop group 3 must be in dead ground, not directly in the killing group's line of fire.

Below: US Marines clear up after a successful ambush in South Vietnam. The search party, commanded by the platoon sergeant in a platoon ambush, checks the enemy dead while sentries maintain all-round observation in case of enemy reaction.

You need patience and good concealment techniques if your ambush is to succeed. It may be possible for you to sit or stand, which will give you a wider field of fire, but you will have to keep very still to avoid being seen.

Combat Report
Vietnam:
Hamburger Hill Part 1

In late 1969, US Marines spent five weeks battling North Vietnamese regulars (NVA) for a desolate, shell-strewn, 880-metre pinnacle known as Hamburger Hill. Jack Meriwether was a Marine lance corporal and rifleman. After a seesaw exchange of gunfire near the peak, Meriwether and his buddies were cut off and surrounded. It was just the beginning.

With two other men, I cringed behind what was left of a wooden bunker on the slope. NVA mortar shells exploded in a crescendo a few metres away, hitting NVA and Marines alike. Flames, shrapnel and smoke filled the air. Shouting, bayonet-carrying NVA raced past above and below us and I realised, in a numb kind of double-take, that the enemy was everywhere . . .

Fellow Marine George Trent stared at me, hard. "There's so damned many people running through the smoke on this hill, nobody is sure who's who. Let's start down and hope we run into our guys."

"No choice," I said. "But they're all around us. Last thing I want is to become a POW."

I looked up from the flimsy protection of the bunker. I saw several NVA charging no more than six metres away. Rifles barked. I felt the impact as a slug careened off my heavy flak jacket. I gripped my M14, fired from the hip, and killed one of the attackers, point-blank.

Nearly 100 men died

"Let's get out of here."

Further down the slope, more enemy blocked our path. Trent, Ray Peters and I stumbled down the long incline, dodging exploding mortar shells and returning NVA rifle fire from point-blank range. At one juncture, we ran straight through a swarm of NVA who didn't seem to notice that we were American Marines.

Nearly 100 men died in the confusion during a period of less than three hours that day. My pals and I were lucky. Racing down the slope, we were swallowed up by our fellow Marines. Only

then did I discover that shrapnel had bloodied my left shoulder.

They wanted to medevac me. My injury seemed to be superficial. We had a platoon leader, Lieutenant Stallings, a gung-ho Annapolis man. I would have followed that lieutenant to hell and back. With my pal Trent at my side, I was beginning to hobble towards the LZ where a chopper was going to evacuate me. We passed the lieutenant's bunker and I heard him barking into a radio. "What do you mean, go back up there?"

"Let's get it done"

At the other end, someone spoke.

"My men are beat," the lieutenant protested. "It's two hours till dark."

Someone spoke again.

"All right, sir. Yes, sir. We'll go back up there again."

I just looked at Trent and moaned, "Aw, . . . ****."

We'd been together a long time, Trent, Peters, the lieutenant, some of the others, and me. We'd broken in most of the newer guys. I turned around, re-slung my M14, and forgot about the medevac. "Let's get it done," I said.

From my point of view, one of the most-publicised and best known battles of the Vietnam War was something of an anticlimax. That afternoon, we had the equivalent of two full battalions assaulting the gnarled, almost barren hill from two directions with the most spectacular air and artillery support that I have ever seen. Our earlier fighting had been like the scenes in that Gregory Peck movie, *Pork Chop Hill*, where the two sides come straight at each other with rifles, grenades, even fixed bayonets. This time, the top brass had decided that we were going to take that goddamned hill, period, and there was going to be no messing around on the way up.

One of the most remarkable sights of my life came in the next few seconds as two Marine aircraft swept in low over the slope and dropped silvery, teardrop-shaped cans of napalm. I think

At Hamburger Hill the North Vietnamese did not break contact and slip away; they stood their ground and fought. Here a Marine is bringing up more ammunition while under fire.

the planes were A-4s, Skyhawks. This time, the brass weren't fooling around . . .

There was the clack-clack! of rifle fire off to our right. Another platoon, halfway up, seemed to have run into NVA on the slope before even getting within 100 metres of the crest. In front of us, the lieutenant was beckoning for us to scatter and get down. I thought he was expecting a similar group of NVA to make contact with us. But the lieutenant knew something I didn't. He'd been briefed on what the Skyhawks were going to do . . .

Troops silhouetted against the sky while fortifying the positions after the battle was over – or so we thought. In fact the NVA launched a series of counter-attacks that led to bitter close-quarter fighting with free use of grenades and even bayonets.

SPRINGING YOUR AMBUSH

You're hardly breathing. The signal's come through at last from one of your flanking groups that the enemy's on his way. A few minutes later and you can see them, making their way cautiously in file toward you along the track below. In seconds they'll inevitably bunch together in that patch of open ground before crossing the stream. They'll never make it. That's the killing ground.

The point man's at the water now. The guy bringing up the rear's obviously an officer. He's not in the killing ground, but he's clear in your sights when the Claymores tear the clearing apart.

The din is unbelievable, what with automatic weapons letting rip on all sides as well, and somebody tossing grenades into the mix just for good measure. You don't hear your own firing, only feel the recoil. You've got your man, and in the clearing it's a shambles. That's the way to do it.

Lying in wait

The business end of a successful ambush can be over in seconds, but waiting for enemy to turn up can be frustrating and tedious. You have to get into position, make yourself as comfortable as possible, and stay put without smoking, moving, talking or making any other noise for as long as it takes to complete the operation.

How long you have to stay in the ambush position depends on where you are. On a cold, rainy winter's night in Europe you're unlikely to be able to wait more than six hours. In any case, you should expect to be relieved or to withdraw within about 12 hours.

Ready for action

Once in position, set up a system that lets some of the group relax while the others watch. Otherwise, concentration will deteriorate fast. But everyone must be prepared for instant action, whether observing or relaxing. Your weapon must be cocked and in position, and grenades placed ready to throw.

When the enemy appears in the killing ground, take careful aim and wait for the signal to fire. It is vitally important that you do not disturb the vegetation or make any rustling noises as you follow the enemy with your sights.

Combat Skills

Civilian targets

You can meet two particularly ticklish problems while waiting to spring an ambush, especially if it's a long-term one: civilians, and friendly troops.

Civilians may well walk through your killing area, or even stop to chat or rest there. All you can do then is lie low and wait for them to go before enemy troops appear.

If you're spotted by a civilian, you really have only two alternatives: detain him – which could create even more problems for a long-term ambush – or lift the ambush and, perhaps, lay it somewhere else.

The enemy may use civilians as porters or guides, intermingled with his patrol. As commander of an ambush you then have an agonising choice to make on the spur of the moment. You may consider that the civilians' very presence in the patrol makes them legitimate targets. On the other hand, killing press-ganged civilians could do enormous damage to relations with the local population.

What you certainly shouldn't do is ask your own soldiers to shoot selectively. The time taken to decide whether or not to take out a particular target could easily cost them their own lives.

Enter friendly troops

In theory a friendly patrol should never pass through an ambush. In practice, it happens only too often: in the Falklands campaign two British patrols clashed and took fatal casualties.

To avoid the worst, you must freeze until the friendly patrol is clear. Don't try to make contact. They may misinterpret any attempt you make to warn them of your presence – possibly with fatal results.

AFTER THE AMBUSH

To search or not to search: this largely depends on the tactical situation and, of course, your orders. If you are a small force operating in enemy territory in conventional war it may not be good sense to spend time on body searching: risk of enemy counter-attack may be too high. You could have just engaged the lead company of an entire Soviet motor rifle regiment on the move!

Packing up
While the searchers are out, ambush lights, comms cord and other equipment should be collected and packed. There should be no indications left of unit identity or standard operational procedures.

Individual weapon sight
Flares and other very bright light sources will make the IWS useless, so sort out beforehand whether you are going to body-search with ambush lights and flares or PNG (passive night goggles), IWS and thermal imagers.

51-mm mortar
This can be used to fire HE into the killing zone or likely avenues of escape, illuminating rounds during killing and search and smoke to cover the withdrawal to the FRV. The mortar would normally be fired from dead ground, ideally under the control of the platoon sergeant in the FRV.

Intelligence-gathering
If you are not going to take the enemy dead with you, search the bodies and take anything that may be of intelligence value. Make sure you label and bag items carefully so that you can tell the intelligence officer which kit came from which body. A quick sketch of who you found where would also be helpful in deciding where enemy patrol commanders usually travel in the patrol, etc.

Kit
Bergens and kit not required for the ambush should be dumped in the FRV. Searchers especially should travel light as they may have to fire and manoeuvre at speed out of the killing zone.

Signals
Radio silence is usually in force until the ambush is sprung. It is vital that you are in communication so that you can call down supporting mortar and artillery fire onto pre-registered DFs, in case of enemy counter-attack or follow up.

When the enemy is ambushed his first priority is to get off the killing ground. Here a US National Guard patrol comes under attack, thus learning the rule that you don't use tracks. But unfortunately there are some tactical situations where you will have to, as travelling cross-country through dense woodland may be too slow and noisy.

Cut-off groups
These must have radio comms with the ambush commander as they may have engaged the scout group of the enemy patrol and need to search. They provide flank protection during the search phase and warn of enemy follow-up.

Breaking contact
Speed is essential to your survival. If you are going to search, do it as fast as possible, followed by a very rapid withdrawal to the FRV with a headcheck and best possible speed on the first few legs of the route back. The enemy may have had time to call for reinforcements or a fire mission on the ambush position.

Searchers
Searchers should usually work in two-man teams. They can be drawn from either the killing group or cut-off group, but should always be covered by the remainder. Each team should be clearly briefed and given time to rehearse beforehand. The teams should be given a specific area or group of bodies to search and limit of exploitation so that there is no chance of them shooting at each other. Torches of the type usually used by poachers to spotlight game, fitted and roughly zeroed to the rifle, are a useful search tool.

Mines
If you have used mines and obstacles to cover escape routes from the ambush position, use the searchers to put them out initially so that they will not then run into them in the dark.

Ambush follow-up
In counter-revolutionary warfare, or ambushing small groups of enemy close to your own FEBA, body searching and follow-up is a more acceptable proposition. Dog teams can be useful for following blood trails to track down those who manage to get out of the killing zone.

POW
A well-laid and executed ambush should not produce any POWs. You must not risk sending searchers into the killing zone without being sure that everything in it is dead or well out of it: this is what the watch-and-shoot phase is for. Make sure you cover the eventuality in your orders and that your POW handling teams are briefed and have POW kit, plasticuffs, hood, gag and all kit ready.

Booby-trapping
In some tactical situations this may be acceptable, if there is time. Booby-trapping enemy bodies and equipment with grenades, Claymores etc may have an adverse effect on enemy morale.

373

1 After the commander calls 'Cease Fire', search parties should check the bodies in the killing zone, looking for anything of intelligence value.

2 Approach a body cautiously, one man covering the moving man just in case the enemy soldier is feigning death.

3 Kick him to make sure he is not simply lying doggo, while your oppo keeps him covered.

Springing your ambush

Carefully plan and rehearse the drill for springing your ambush. The usual pattern is this:

The cut-off group that sights the enemy signals to the ambush commander. You will need a pre-arranged system so that you can communicate the size and direction of the enemy party at the same time.

You alert all the other groups in the ambush with the same information. Everyone must now – silently and invisibly – take up a firing position.

Wait until the maximum number of enemy is in the killing area. Then spring the ambush – either by opening fire yourself, or by tapping the machine gunner next to you on the shoulder, so that he opens fire.

Obviously, you need to put down the maximum possible weight of fire immediately. Perhaps the best way of achieving this is to sow the killing ground with Claymore mines, and spring the ambush by detonating them electrically. The effect can be quite devastating.

The follow-up

Once you've sprung the ambush, the action is usually intense and short. Any remnants of a numerically weak enemy will normally run. But you will usually be able to destroy even a strong enemy, given your advantages of surprise, concentrated firepower and position.

When enemy movement has ceased, give the signal to stop firing. Then wait. Everyone must still be in the aim and fully alert. At this stage enemy survivors will often try to run. Look out for any wounded enemy who may be still able to use a grenade on anyone approaching them.

If there is no further movement, shout 'Cease fire!' You can now move into the killing ground to search the enemy for documents or any other intelligence. At night you will not normally be able to do this, since one of your groups could take another for enemy. Your next job then is to withdraw.

Enemy reaction

If you ambush a very much larger enemy force, you'd be wise to follow a 'shoot and scoot' procedure. In the first place, use only Claymore mines to engage the enemy so that he cannot pinpoint your position, and call in artillery fire to cover your withdrawal.

Almost certainly, not all the enemy will have been in the killing area, and the remaining forces will react by launching an immediate assault into the killing group.

men with you who are difficult to move. This sort of reaction is more likely to be possible in counter-insurgency operations than in conventional warfare.

Vehicles under attack

If your convoy is ambushed, the vehicles caught in the ambush must return fire immediately, while the vehicle commander makes a rapid decision whether to drive out or fight.

If it is to fight, then he must dismount and put in an attack. When the vehicle commander shouts, 'Dismount Left (or Right)', you must follow him. The sentries simultaneously throw smoke grenades and return fire. Then mount a quick counter-attack.

You should always drive out of the ambush if you can, but this may not be possible if your path is blocked by disabled vehicles or your driver is injured.

If you are in a vehicle that has not been caught in the ambush, it is your job to halt the vehicle, drive it off the road if possible, muster all available men and mount a counter-attack to relieve those caught in the ambush. It is of course crucially important that you know where you are all the time, so that you can indicate over the radio to artillery, aircraft or a relieving force where to produce the support you need. Continuous map reading by commanders on any move is therefore vital.

Vehicle commanders
The vehicle commander must travel in the back of the vehicle because if the troops have to dismount to counter-attack an ambush, he will be leading them. An experienced soldier or NCO rides shotgun next to the driver.

Alertness
All vehicles must have vehicle sentries with automatic weapons who take immediate action from the vehicle if they are ambushed. You can fire 84-mm anti-tank weapons, GPMGs and light mortars from most vehicles: the aim is maximum firepower to suppress the ambushers.

Riding shotgun
An NCO should sit next to the driver of each vehicle, ready to assist him. If the troops dismount and leave the vehicle, the 'shotgun' man stays behind with the driver to protect the vehicle.

Convoy command
A vehicle convoy must have a commander positioned where he can best control the column of vehicles. Action in case of an ambush must be detailed clearly in advance: if you are attacked, there is no time for hesitation.

Security
If you are travelling through guerrilla-infested country, or when the population is hostile, you must pay careful regard to the security of your convoy plans. Always vary your routes and timing; do not issue your orders until the last possible moment; and make sure you have a deception plan to fool the guerrillas into staking out the wrong road.

PREPARING YOUR VEHICLE

You must have all-round observation, and you must be able to fire and throw grenades from the vehicle and debus with your fighting order in quick time. Here are a few useful modifications.

1 Get rid of any superstructure that restricts arcs of observation or fire.
2 Unarmoured vehicles should be sandbagged against mines and up-armoured if possible.
3 Travel with the tailboard down or removed.
4 Add GPMG mounts to all unarmed vehicles.
5 High wire cutters should be fitted to all vehicles. Also, if you have the means, fit metal grids to the front of the vehicle so that you can cruise through light barricades.
6 No more than 15 men should travel in the back of a four-tonner, sitting facing out and to the rear.
7 Fit towing bars to all the vehicles, and make sure full tool kits are carried, along with mine detectors and rope for clearing obstacles.

It is no good pretending that there is any magic solution to being caught in an ambush. But, whether you are on foot or in a vehicle, it is possible to turn the tables on the ambushers if your drills are good and if you have the courage to take the offensive when you are at a disadvantage.

Exploit enemy errors

If the enemy mistimes his ambush so that only part of your force is affected, he makes your job a great deal easier. The part of your patrol that is ambushed should extricate itself as best it can, until it can bring some force to bear on the ambusher.

In this way they can produce fire to keep the enemy's heads down, while you organise a counter-attack with those of your force not caught in the ambush. If you have air or artillery support, use it. However, if this would delay your counter-attack, you should probably do without it. Your priority must be to relieve the ambushed part of your force as quickly as possible.

A night ambush is difficult to mount

Smoke, preferably in the form of white phosphorus, is an essential part of any anti-ambush drill. You may be able to throw it far enough to inflict casualties on the enemy.

and, except on the brightest nights, usually requires instant white light at the precise moment of springing the ambush. Get out of the illuminated area as quickly as you can.

It will be much more difficult to retain control of your men at night. There can be no question of a flanking or encircling counter-attack at night because of the difficulty of control in a confused situation.

Out-think the enemy

A clever enemy will try to work out your likely reaction to the initial burst of fire, and he will try and thwart your next move. He may well lay anti-personnel mines in obvious reorganisation positions, or site Claymore mines to cover escape routes. The enemy – if he is any good – will aim in the opening volleys of an ambush to kill commanders and radio operators to

increase confusion.

Obviously, therefore, commanders and signallers should not make themselves conspicuous by their dress or behaviour. They should not march at a set place in the column, they should not carry a different weapon and they should not wear badges of rank. Unless you are actually using your radio, antennae should not be mounted.

Stay alert

You should make it difficult or impossible for the enemy to ambush your whole force simultaneously. You must remain well spaced out, alert and suspicious, so that you stand the maximum chance of surviving an ambush.

Finally, you should be constantly thinking of where the current RV is in the event of an ambush. This can either be the location of the last long halt or a set distance back from the rear of the column (say 400 metres). This latter arrangement is suitable only if your force is of platoon size or smaller.

Protecting vehicles

There are some additional and different actions required if you are ambushed in a vehicle.

If you are in an unarmoured vehicle, you can take several precautions against the threat of mines. You can sandbag the floor of the vehicle, you can remove glass, doors, the canopy and the cross bars holding up the canopy, and you can get your vehicle mechanics to fit mineplating.

In Northern Ireland the British Army has fitted Glass Reinforced Plastic (GRP) and macralon armouring to

VEHICLE ANTI-AMBUSH DRILL

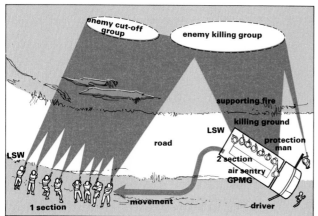

On contact, the vehicle commander or whoever sees it first and is not hit by the initial burst shouts 'ambush left' or 'ambush right' as appropriate, and everyone immediately returns fire. If the vehicle is not hit then the driver should drive through.

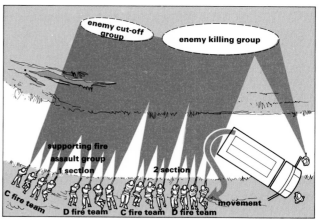

Those on the same side of the ambush stay on the vehicle and give covering fire, while those on the other side get off and move into cover by fire and manoeuvre, preferably led by the group commander.

AMBUSH DRILLS ON FOOT

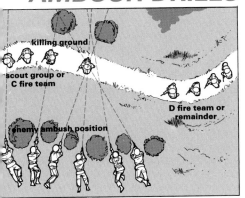

killing ground

scout group or C fire team

enemy ambush position

D fire team or remainder

Left: If you are patrolling with a tactical bound between fire teams or scout group and main body, the enemy may not contact the whole patrol, in which case the survivors of the group in contact return fire and indicate the location of the enemy by voice or radio.

Right: The remainder then assault the enemy position by fire and manoeuvre. The faster you do this the better, so learn to recognise likely ambush positions and the type of ground commonly selected.

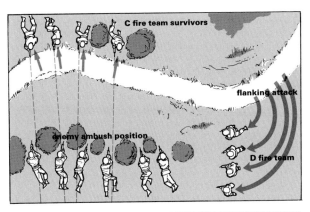

C fire team survivors

flanking attack

enemy ambush position

D fire team

the sides and windscreens of its Land Rovers. While not stopping high velocity rounds, it will mitigate the effects of low velocity rounds, shrapnel and blast fragments.

Don't sit next to the driver but in the rear of the vehicle where you can see and command your men. If there is a cupola in the roof of the vehicle cab, put a man with a rifle or, better still, manning a mounted GPMG there, where he has a good view of the road ahead and from where he can produce automatic fire at any ambushers.

If you are a passenger in the back of the vehicle, it is better to fit the two rows of benches in the centre, so that you can sit back to back facing outwards. That way you are watching the side of the road for potential ambush sites and can react and debus more quickly. Nominate a number of men to hold smoke grenades (preferably phosphorus, which produce instant smoke), which they can throw to create a smoke screen between the ambushers and your vehicle.

ALTERNATIVE ANTI-AMBUSH DRILL

1 If the whole patrol is caught in the killing zone, your only option is to immediately charge the ambushers: the quickest way out of the killing ground is to get behind the weapons that are firing on you.

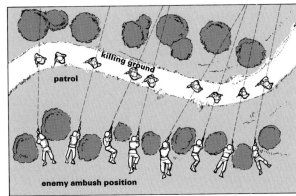

killing ground

patrol

enemy ambush position

2 On contact, turn into the ambush and charge it, firing at the weapon flashes. The key to success is instant, very heavy volume of fire, including 66-mm or RPG if you are lucky enough to have it, fired into the general area of the enemy killer group.

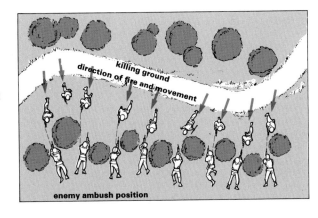

killing ground

direction of fire and movement

enemy ambush position

3 Once you are in the ambush position, turn to face the direction from which you have come. Run along the line of the enemy positions behind the weapon flashes and fire down on anyone on the ground. Do not fire forwards.

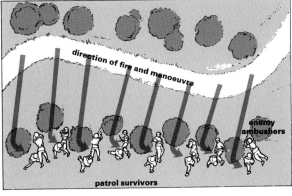

direction of fire and manoeuvre

enemy ambushers

patrol survivors

enemy cut off group

enemy killing group

flanking attack

unit commander

protection man

fire support group 2 section

C fire team

D fire team

driver

The first fire team or group off then provide cover while the others debus. This group then becomes the fire support for the flanking attack on the enemy ambush position. 84-mm and perhaps an extra LSW may be left with the fire support group.

Unarmed Combat Course No. 21
DEFENCE AGAINST ARMED ATTACKERS Part 1

In this sequence the defender faces two attackers, both armed with knives. You must remember that the knife is at its most dangerous when close, so you need as much room as possible for an effective defence. Remember: *never use a real knife when practising these techniques.*

1 You are confronted by an attacker armed with a knife. Note how he is holding it: will he stab or slash?

2 The attacker prepares to slash you with the knife; you move your hands up for a forearm block.

3 Block his returning arm ready to apply an outside wristlock.

4 Close-up of the forearm block about to move into a wristlock.

5 As usual your thumbs should be together, gripping the attacker's hand.

6 You use the wristlock to force the attacker over on to his back, just as the second attacker makes his move.

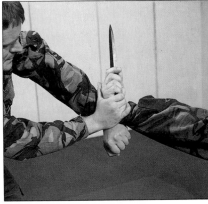

8 Close-up of the X block in action: the two forearms stop the forward movement of the knife.

7 The second attacker tries to stab you but you block the knife thrust with an X block against his wrist. Note how the defender shoots his most vulnerable parts to the rear, presenting as small a target as possible.

9 Now you move from the block to the wristlock, one hand on his knife hand and then the other.

10 With the wristlock applied you can control the attacker, bringing him forward and down, ready to be counter-attacked.

11 Follow up with a kick to finish him off and seize the attackers' weapons.

Unarmed Combat Course No. 22

DEFENCE AGAINST ARMED ATTACKERS
Part 2

In these two sequences the defender faces a mixture of armed attackers and demonstrates a series of defensive moves. In many cases you need to seize the attacker's weapon, but if you actually use it in a civilian situation you could face prosecution. *Never use real weapons in practice sessions.*

Cosh and strangle attack

1 You are attacked from behind and the attacker tries to strangle you.

2 Free yourself by reaching down and grabbing the attacker's testicles while hanging on to his strangling arm.

3 Attacker no. 2 has pulled out a cosh, so you finish off the first attacker with a shoulder throw.

4 Attacker no. 2 comes running forward ready to strike you, but you are leaning forward after the shoulder throw.

6 Now swing back upwards using the attacker's momentum to help propel him into the air and over your shoulder.

5 Taking advantage of your position, move in low as the attacker reaches you, your right arm going under his legs as your left arm deflects the cosh.

Knife and pistol attack

1 You are facing a direct-thrust knife attack from the front. Remember that a 'wimpish' response may tempt the attacker into over-confidence.

2 Deflect the knife thrust upwards using your left hand, then bring your right hand to join the left and fix the attacker in an outside wristlock.

3 Fling the attacker over onto his back, ready to seize the weapon and finish him off.

4 But you can't finish him off; a second attacker sticks the muzzle of a pistol into your back and orders you to give up.

5 The attacker has come too close so you attack without hesitation, pivoting to the side and striking the pistol away from you.

6 Apply an outside wristlock and give attacker no. 2 the same treatment, landing him on his back.

7 This time you can seize the weapon and take control. Remember that you can still be vulnerable if you pick up a weapon that you are unfamiliar with. It is important to get to know how to use all common infantry weapons, including the main foreign small arms.

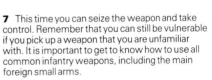

GOING TO THE RESCUE
PART 1

When going to someone's rescue, don't forget that the victim of the attacker is unlikely to be instantly of use to you. You are therefore in a one-to-one situation, so make sure you exploit the initial advantage of surprise with efficient technique.

Armpit lock and control

1 The victim is being strangled against a wall. You approach the attacker from behind, ready to block if the attacker turns and punches you.

2 Push your right arm under the attacker's armpit and across his chest. Clasp your right hand in your left.

3 With the lock in place, tuck your head well in to avoid a blow.

4 The preceding action should be one continuous movement. Then use your body weight and momentum to force the attacker down so that you can control him.

Wristlock, throw down and control

1 Again the attacker has the victim in a stranglehold. Both the attacker's hands are exposed. Approach from behind and move in on the left.

2 Apply the wristlock to the attacker's exposed hand. This will break his grip.

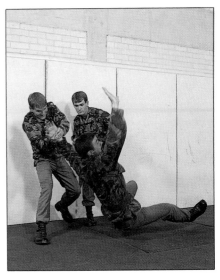

3 Rotate the attacker's arm backwards and the rest of him is bound to follow. Practise this in slow motion only.

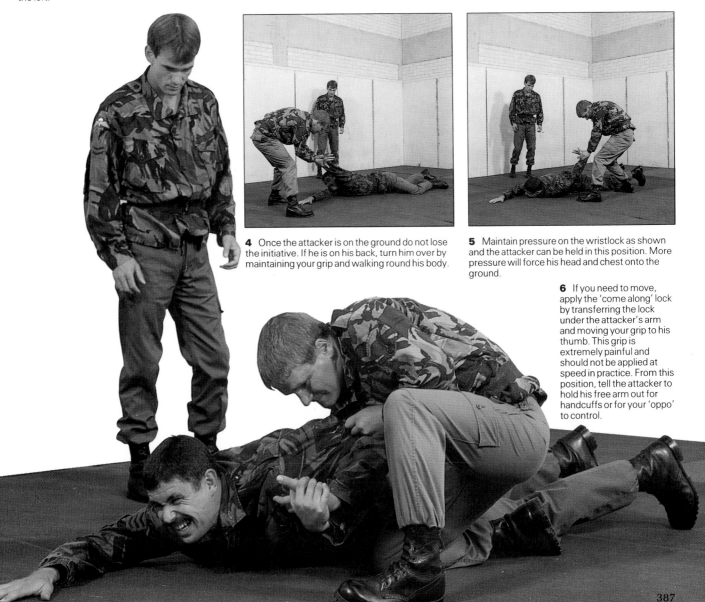

4 Once the attacker is on the ground do not lose the initiative. If he is on his back, turn him over by maintaining your grip and walking round his body.

5 Maintain pressure on the wristlock as shown and the attacker can be held in this position. More pressure will force his head and chest onto the ground.

6 If you need to move, apply the 'come along' lock by transferring the lock under the attacker's arm and moving your grip to his thumb. This grip is extremely painful and should not be applied at speed in practice. From this position, tell the attacker to hold his free arm out for handcuffs or for your 'oppo' to control.

Tank-Busting with MILAN

MILAN is the world's leading anti-tank missile, and has been in service with the British Army since the mid 1970s. Built by a Franco-German consortium called Euromissile, the weapon uses a highly accurate Semi-Automatic Command to Line of Sight (SACLOS) guidance system that makes MILAN as easy to shoot as a rifle – with vastly more devastating effect. Some 30 nations use MILAN: over 50,000 missiles have been fired, scoring a 94 per cent rate of kills.

MILAN is designed to be used by a two-man team on the ground, although it can also be installed in armoured vehicles. The basic model uses a 'firing post' consisting of a sight unit on a small tripod and a complete missile pre-packed at the factory into a glass-fibre launch tube. The loader places the launch tube on to supports on the launcher post, which automatically connects the missile electronics to the sight unit.

Aiming the weapon

The operator then aims the weapon through the optical sight, placing the crosshairs of the sight on the centre of his target, and squeezes the trigger. A small explosive charge in the launch tube blows the missile out, and then a rocket motor in the missile ignites and it accelerates away, trailing a wire behind it. This wire is connected to the sight unit. The operator now keeps his sight on the target.

How it works

The missile carries an infra-red flare in its tail. This flare is detected by a special sensor inside the sight, and its position is automatically measured. This position is then compared with the axis of the sight, and any difference is signalled to a micro-computer in the sight unit. The computer sends any necessary corrections to the flight path as signals down the trailing wire. These signals are received in the missile and are used to push a spoiler plate into the rocket jet, so steering the missile to one side or another, up or down, until the missile is flying exactly on target. This process goes on until the missile hits the target.

MILAN flies at about 200 metres per second, and it will range to 2000 metres. At this speed it cannot do

A MILAN anti-tank guided missile is launched. The launching tube flies backwards off the firing post as the missile blasts off towards the target.

Firing the MILAN

The No. 1 from a MILAN team of 2nd Battalion, Royal Irish Rangers, tells how it's done:

"Both my No. 2 and I are ready. A missile is fitted to the firing post but not loaded. A target appears in our killing area. I tell the No. 2 to load. He then fully fits the missile to the firing post and checks that the back blast area is clear. Then he shouts "LOADED!"

"I take over then, lifting the double safety flap and exposing the firing button. I pre-aim the weapon at the target, placing what appears as a crow's foot over the target, then fire the missile. Pre-aiming is necessary to allow for the weight of the missile leaving the launching post: after the missile has been fired the crosshairs of the sights automatically drop to wherever I placed the pre-aiming mark.

"Now I must keep the crosshairs on the *part* of the vehicle I want the missile to strike. The missile climbs to begin with, then, after a couple of hundred metres, it comes under my complete control. There is little noise when firing the weapon; all you hear is a pop as the rocket motor fires and then a 'whoosh' as it speeds off towards the target. I like this system because it's easy to use and so accurate that you'd need both hands tied behind your back to miss with it."

"You'd need both hands tied behind your back to miss with it!" according to the MILAN platoon of 2 R Irish. Here the No. 1 takes aim with the MIRA sight while the No. 2 observes the target area.

MILAN's shaped charge warhead can penetrate the armour of any tank in service, and it is so accurate that the gunner can choose which part of the tank he wants to hit.

MILAN is fired from an FV432 APC during British Army tests. Travelling at 200 metres per second, MILAN is nearly twice as fast as the first-generation portable missiles.

This member of the MILAN team is carrying the 16-kg firing post and holding the 9-mm Sterling sub-machine gun, which is used for close-in defence of their position.

MILAN is designed to be fired in all weathers. The battery in each missile is self-activating, and is designed for long-term storage and for use in a wide variety of climates.

The tube flies backwards from the launching post as the missile begins its flight. The gas generator in the tube burns for just 45 milliseconds: enough to fire the missile and hurl the tube about 2 metres.

The British Army has been evaluating this twin MILAN launcher fitted to a Spartan APC. In addition to the pair of ready-to-fire missiles, another eight are carried inside the vehicle.

389

much damage by its own impact, so it relies on a specially designed warhead to blast a hole in the tank's armour. The warhead contains a charge of powerful high explosive, the front of which is hollowed out into a cone. This causes the explosive blast to be focussed, rather like a beam of light, into a fine jet. The cone is lined with metal, which is vapourised and adds body to the jet. This explosive jet, moving at something like 10,000 metres per second, will blow a hole in one metre of armour plate at any range.

MILAN has seen some improvements since it first entered service. The sight can now be fitted with the MIRA (MILAN Infra-Red Attachment) night sight. This is a self-contained unit that clamps on top of the sight

Inside the MILAN

It takes about 13 seconds for the MILAN missile to reach its maximum range of 2000 metres. As it flies towards the target an infra-red flare in its tail is monitored by the sight unit on the firing post, and all the operator has to do is to place the crosshairs on his sight over the part of the enemy tank he wishes to hit. Whatever the range, the explosive jet produced when the warhead hits a tank will burn through a metre of NATO heavy armour plate.

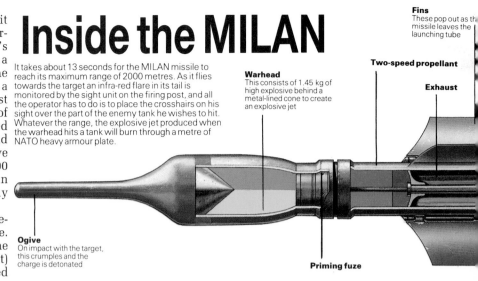

Fins
These pop out as the missile leaves the launching tube

Two-speed propellant

Exhaust

Warhead
This consists of 1.45 kg of high explosive behind a metal-lined cone to create an explosive jet

Priming fuze

Ogive
On impact with the target, this crumples and the charge is detonated

MILAN Platoon

It takes the best part of £3 million to equip a MILAN platoon. So, as you might imagine, MILAN teams have to be a bit special. Each missile costs about £11,000 so a firing post operator is only allowed to fire one live missile a year; the rest of the time you train on a simulator. Despite its hi-tech capabilities, the MILAN is robust and soldier-proof, and doubled as an excellent bunker-buster during the Falklands conflict.

The Detachment

Each detachment consists of five men: a corporal commanding two firing posts; one operated by a lance-corporal and a private, the other by two privates.

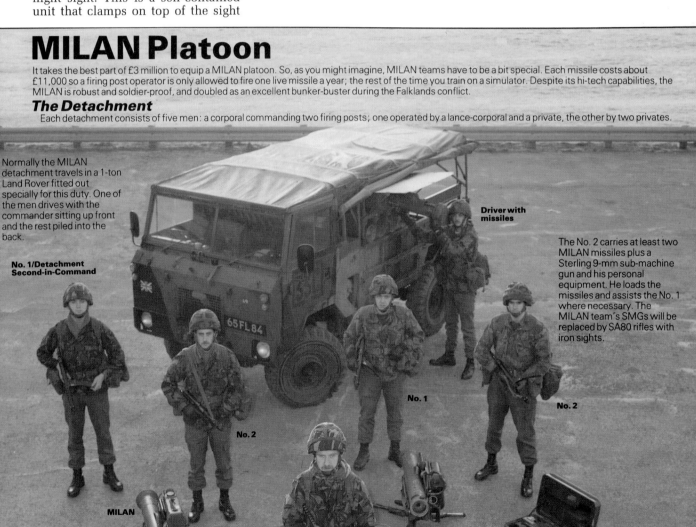

Normally the MILAN detachment travels in a 1-ton Land Rover fitted out specially for this duty. One of the men drives with the commander sitting up front and the rest piled into the back.

Driver with missiles

The No. 2 carries at least two MILAN missiles plus a Sterling 9-mm sub-machine gun and his personal equipment. He loads the missiles and assists the No. 1 where necessary. The MILAN team's SMGs will be replaced by SA80 rifles with iron sights.

No. 1/Detachment Second-in-Command

No. 2

No. 1

No. 2

MILAN

The lance-corporal is second-in-command of the detachment and is No. 1 on one of the firing posts. It is the No. 1's job to carry the firing post along with its MIRA thermal image sight, plus an SA80 rifle and full CEFO (Combat Equipment Fighting Order: at least 16 kg of kit).

Detachment Commander

MILAN with MIRA fitted

MIRA in suitcase

The corporal is responsible for training the detachment. He does his share of the carrying too. His personal load usually exceeds 30 kg and includes the unit's VHF radio.

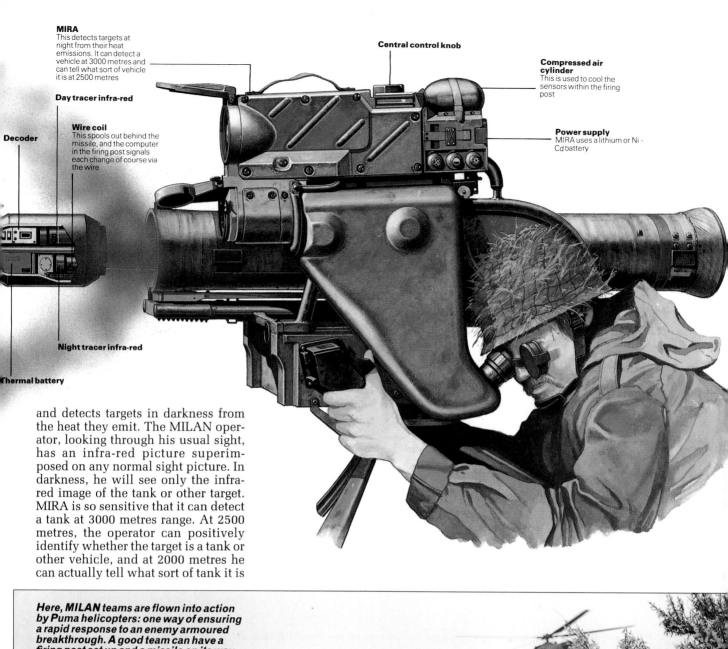

MIRA
This detects targets at night from their heat emissions. It can detect a vehicle at 3000 metres and can tell what sort of vehicle it is at 2500 metres

Central control knob

Compressed air cylinder
This is used to cool the sensors within the firing post

Day tracer infra-red

Wire coil
This spools out behind the missile, and the computer in the firing post signals each change of course via the wire

Decoder

Power supply
MIRA uses a lithium or Ni - Cd battery

Night tracer infra-red

Thermal battery

and detects targets in darkness from the heat they emit. The MILAN operator, looking through his usual sight, has an infra-red picture superimposed on any normal sight picture. In darkness, he will see only the infra-red image of the tank or other target. MIRA is so sensitive that it can detect a tank at 3000 metres range. At 2500 metres, the operator can positively identify whether the target is a tank or other vehicle, and at 2000 metres he can actually tell what sort of tank it is

Here, MILAN teams are flown into action by Puma helicopters: one way of ensuring a rapid response to an enemy armoured breakthrough. A good team can have a firing post set up and a missile on its way to the target in 12 seconds.

The Launch

1 The launch tube containing the missile is fitted to the firing post.
2 On firing, the missile is expelled from the tube and its fins pop out to control its flight.
3 The empty tube flies backwards off the firing post and the missile's own motor ignites.
4 The missile climbs for the first 200 m then speeds towards the target, guided by signals passed along the wire.

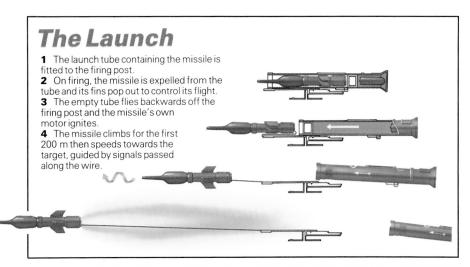

and, if it is enemy, can open fire.

The MIRA attachment has an additional, daylight, use. If, for example, there are tanks concealed behind a screen of bushes at the edge of a wood, the MILAN operator might scan the wood with his normal sight and see nothing. But the MIRA sight will detect the heat given off by the tanks and superimpose their images on the ordinary scene in the optical sight. Thus the operator can detect tanks which would otherwise be invisible to him. It can also detect men, thus providing useful general information on the battle front.

Battlefield Evaluation: comparing

MILAN

MILAN is the best of the second generation of wire-guided anti-tank missiles: it is primarily designed to be used by infantry firing from a defensive position. Produced by Euromissile, a Franco-German consortium, it is manufactured under licence in the UK, and the Soviets are now using a missile which looks suspiciously like a copy, the AT-4 'Spigot'. The missiles come in factory-sealed tubes which are fitted to the firing post; on firing, a gas generator inside the tube blows the missile forwards and, after it has travelled a safe distance from the firing post, the missile's own motor powers it on its 13-second flight to the target.

Specification:
Missile weight: 11.3 kg
Launcher weight: 6.4 kg
Warhead: 1.45 kg shaped-charge high explosive
Minimum range: 25 m
Maximum range: 2000 m
Armour penetration: 1000 mm+

Assessment
Reliability ★★★★
Accuracy ★★★★★
Age ★★
Worldwide users ★★

Seen here in French service, MILAN is the best man-portable anti-tank guided missile available.

MBB Cobra

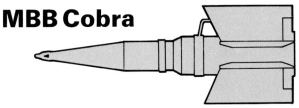

This German missile is typical of the first generation of anti-tank guided weapons which are now obsolete. The missile is placed on the ground, pointing towards the target; up to eight can be connected to the same control box. On firing, the missile is boosted vertically into the air, then its own sustainer cuts in to propel it towards the target. The operator controls it with a joy stick on his control box connected to the missile by a wire. It requires considerable concentration to control the rapidly moving missile and steer it onto the target, and if the operator comes under enemy fire he is unlikely to score a hit.

Specification:
Missile weight: 10.3 kg at launch
Launcher weight: not applicable
Warhead: 7 kg shaped-charge high explosive
Minimum range: 400 m
Maximum range: 2000 m
Armour penetration: 500 mm

Assessment
Reliability ★★
Accuracy ★★
Age ★★★★★
Worldwide users ★★★★

Cobra is no longer in production, but remains in service with some 16 countries, including Argentina.

Bofors BILL

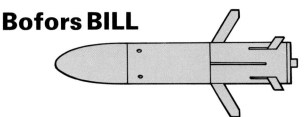

Properly known as the Bofors RBS-56, BILL means 'Bofors, Infantry, Light and Lethal'. BILL is programmed to fly exactly one metre above the sight line and across the top of the tank. A proximity fuse detects the target electronically and automatically fires the warhead when it is within lethal range. The explosive jet shoots down through the thin roof of the tank, with devastating effect on the interior. BILL is in use by the Swedish Army and a number have just been purchased by the American Army for evaluation. BILL has a maximum range of 2000 metres.

Specification:
Missile weight: 16 kg
Launcher weight: 27 kg
Warhead: shaped charge pointing downwards
Minimum range: 150 m
Maximum range: 2000 m
Armour penetration: classified

Assessment
Reliability ★★★★
Accuracy ★★★★
Age ★
Worldwide users ★

This imaginative Swedish missile flies up to attack the thinner armour on the top of a tank.

The Annual Test

Because the cost of live missiles allows only one live firing a year for each operator, no-one can afford to take it lightly. As MILAN's sighting and guidance systems are so accurate, you are placed under a good deal of pressure before firing. Anyone can shoot well in calm conditions on a range, but combat conditions are rarely so kind. The annual test shoot takes place immediately after you have completed an 8-mile 'bash' carrying all your equipment (weighing up to 35 kg) and wearing NBC kit over your normal clothing. You must complete the course in under 1 hour 50 minutes, and then set up the MILAN system and engage a target at maximum range. From a standing start a good team will have the equipment sorted out and a missile on its way in 12 seconds. They rarely miss.

Right: MILAN teams carry a great weight of kit – here the detachment commander accompanies one firing team with their firing post and two missiles. All men carry Sterling 9-mm sub-machine guns for self-defence.

the MILAN with its rivals

AT-3 'Sagger'

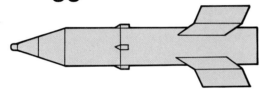

Specification:
Missile weight: 11.3 kg
Launcher weight: not applicable
Warhead: 3 kg HEAT
Minimum range: 300 m
Maximum range: 3000 m
Armour penetration: 410 mm+

'Sagger' is the NATO reference name for this Soviet anti-tank guided missile, which appears in Warsaw Pact and Soviet-equipped armies both as an infantry weapon and mounted on vehicles and helicopters. Egyptian infantry using 'Sagger' inflicted a surprise defeat on the Israeli armoured forces in the first days of the 1973 Arab-Israeli war, but the Israelis rapidly developed countermeasures. Early 'Saggers' were manually controlled and difficult to use when under fire, but in the late 1970s the Soviets introduced a version with semi-automatic guidance.

Assessment	
Reliability	✶✶
Accuracy	✶✶
Age	✶✶✶
Worldwide users	✶✶✶✶

'Sagger' is in service with the Warsaw Pact armies and most Soviet-equipped countries.

Hughes TOW

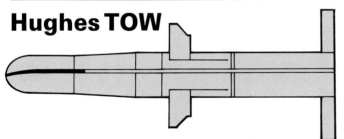

Specification: TOW 2
Missile weight: 28 kg
Launcher weight: 93 kg
Warhead: 5.9 kg
Minimum range: 65 m
Maximum range: 3750 m
Armour penetration: 800 mm+

The only serious competitor to MILAN, TOW is the standard US anti-tank missile. Much bigger and heavier, it works in the same way, tracking an infra-red flare and sending course corrections via a wire. It was used successfully in Vietnam, the 1973 Arab-Israeli war and the 1982 Israeli invasion of Lebanon, and now equips over 30 armies throughout the world.

Assessment	
Reliability	✶✶✶✶
Accuracy	✶✶✶✶
Age	✶✶
Worldwide users	✶✶✶✶

MILAN's only serious rival, TOW is really too large and heavy for the infantry role.

McDonnell Douglas Dragon

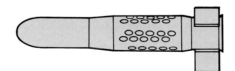

Specification:
Missile weight: 6.2 kg
Launcher weight: 7.6 kg
Warhead: 2.45 kg
Minimum range: 75 m
Maximum range: 1000 m
Armour penetration: 600 mm

This is another American missile system, lighter than TOW and with a range of only 1000 metres. Unusual for its flight guidance: instead of fins or jet spoilers, the missile carries 60 side-thrust rocket motors on its outer surface, and rolls as it flies. A central rocket gives forward thrust. As side-thrust rockets reach bottom centre, they fire in turn to give lift. They can also be fired by signals sent down the wire to steer the missile in the correct direction. Dragon's reliability and accuracy have recently been questioned and there are moves afoot to replace it.

Assessment	
Reliability	✶✶✶
Accuracy	✶✶
Age	✶✶✶
Worldwide users	✶✶✶

Light but short-ranged, Dragon is probably not powerful enough to take on the latest Soviet armour.

Battling with the BMP

The BMP was built to allow Soviet infantry to keep attacking at high speed even during a nuclear war. Combined forces of Main Battle Tanks and infantry in BMPs are trained to smash through the enemy defences and continue to advance at a cracking pace, 70 to 100 km a day. The enemy is never given time to recover, and the fast moving Soviet armour is never halted long enough to be targeted by tactical nuclear weapons.

When the BMP (Boyevaya Mashina Pekhoty) made its first public appearance in Moscow at the October Revolution Parade of 1967, it immediately became clear that the Warsaw Pact now possessed an armoured personnel carrier superior in every respect to anything in the NATO arsenals.

Although the BMP was small by Western standards, its 280 6-cylinder engine was nevertheless powerful enough to match the latest Soviet main battle tanks in cross-country performance, and its crew compartment large enough to accommodate an eight-man section of fully-equipped infantrymen.

Design history

The Red Army learned from the bloodbaths of 1943 and 1944 that massed tank attacks invariably end in failure unless supported by infantry capable of exploiting any breaches in the enemy defences. At that time, rifle sections were carried forward into battle on the unprotected hulls of T-34

The majority of Soviet and Warsaw Pact infantry ride into battle in the BMP mechanized infantry combat vehicle. Light and fast, the BMP is fully amphibious although its low silhouette makes it easily swamped in choppy water.

was fine in theory, but suicidal in practice. It is now more than likely that the Soviets will debus some 200–300 metres from the enemy position, completing the assault on foot under the covering fire of the stationary AFVs, and the BMP remains an excellent vehicle for such purposes.

The BMP has been one of the greatest successes of Soviet post-war military technology and even now, some 20 years after its introduction, it remains one of the best mechanised infantry combat vehicles in service.

The BMP needs a gently sloping river bank in order to get back onto dry land. The trim vane seen here helps its stability in the water.

the BMP with its rivals

Bradley

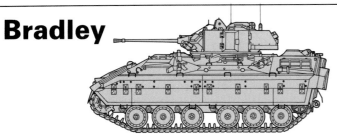

Designed to beat the BMP at its own game, the Bradley is very fast cross-country, very heavily armed and very expensive. Its armour protection falls far short of the original requirements and is vulnerable to the BMP's missiles and the 30-mm cannon of the BMP-2. Increasing the Bradley's armour has made it too heavy, and as several have sunk while trying to cross rivers the Americans may have to choose between amphibious capability and armour protection.

Specification:
Combat weight: 22.5 tonnes
Road speed: 66 km/h
Power to weight ratio: 20 hp/tonne
Length: 6.45 m
Height: 2.97 m
Crew: 3+7
Armament: 1×25-mm cannon; 1×7.62-mm machine-gun; 2 × TOW missile launchers

Assessment
Firepower	★★★★★
Protection	★★★
Age	★
Worldwide users	★

By trying to make it superior in every way, the Americans have made the Bradley an expensive mistake.

MCV-80 Warrior

Twenty-five years after the Soviets developed their mechanized infantry tactics, the British Army is preparing to fight with an Infantry Combat Vehicle. Like the BMP-2, Warrior will rely on a high-velocity 30-mm cannon that can penetrate the armour of rival IFVs, but British infantry will continue to rely on dismounted Milan teams for anti-tank defence since Warrior does not carry a missile armament.

Specification:
Combat weight: 24.5 tonnes
Road speed: 75 km/h
Power to weight ratio: 22.5 hp/tonne
Length: 6.34 m
Height: 2.73 m
Crew: 3+7
Armament: 1×30-mm RARDEN cannon; 1×7.62-mm Chain Gun

Assessment
Firepower	★★★★★
Protection	★★★
Age	★
Worldwide users	★

MCV-80 is better armoured than the BMP but has no amphibious capability.

M113

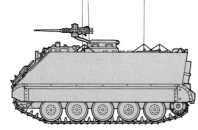

Serving with over 50 countries, the M113 will probably soldier on to the end of the century. It is far more comfortable than the new generation of IFVs, which from the BMP to the Bradley and Warrior are very cramped indeed. On the other hand, the extra room is reflected by extra height: the M113 presents a much larger target to enemy weapons, and its lack of a cannon would leave it helpless if faced by a BMP.

Specification:
Combat weight: 11 tonnes
Road speed: 67 km/h
Power to weight ratio: 67 hp/tonne
Length: 4.86 m
Height: 2.5 m
Crew: 3+11
Armament: 1×0.50-cal machine-gun

Assessment
Firepower	★
Protection	★★
Age	★★★★★
Worldwide users	★★★★★

Still the most numerous APC, the M113 is more roomy and better protected than the BMP.

Getting Heavy with the Hercules

What is the world's greatest military aircraft? In terms of longevity, versatility or numbers, few can rival the Lockheed Hercules. The prototype first flew in August 1954 and Hercules are still in production 33 years later, and still flying with a bewildering variety of air arms. This 'do-it-all' airlifter began life in the early 1950s as a project to provide the US Air Force with a tactical turboprop transport that could utilise short, rough-field strips to carry large and bulky loads.

Adopting what has now become the standard tactical transport layout, the Hercules has its wings set high to allow a rear loading ramp and not to impinge on cabin space; low-pressure tyres, mounted on the side of the fuselage, for rough-field operations; and a simple circular cabin with an

Left: Paratroops emerge from the side doors of a USAF Hercules. Mass drops such as this are a regular feature of US exercises.

Right: The unmistakable nose of the MC-130 reveals an enlarged radome for the terrain avoidance radar, and retracted forks for the Fulton recovery system – both used for clandestine Special Forces operations.

immensely strong floor. High lift devices on the wings and four powerful engines complete the picture.

Vietnam success

Entering service in late 1956, the C-130, as it was designated by the US Air Force, was soon living up to its name, proving excellent in many areas of transport, from landing in extremely short fields to trans-Atlantic freight runs. In Vietnam, the type was widely used, and its short-field performance was often called into use as it resupplied outlying camps.

Current tactical airlift and assault tactics were largely forged in Vietnam, often as a result of withering small-arms fire from the VC guerrillas surrounding US airfields. A popular

feature in any Hercules air display is the 'Khe Sanh' approach, flying high to avoid groundfire before a spectacularly steep dive to a couple of metres before a gut-wrenching flare to land. All four propellers are then thrust into reverse-pitch, bringing the giant Hercules to a halt with a roar and clouds of dust. The rear ramp opens and troops, guns and vehicles emerge at the double, immediately setting up defensive positions.

All aircraft are vulnerable on the ground, so the Hercules can either turn round on a sixpence or back up with reverse pitch to give it the room to take off again, usually using a steep climb-out and steep banking to avoid the dangers of groundfire. Such operations are the speciality of the Hercules, and there are none better.

Operations from semi-prepared strips are the Hercules' forte, demonstrated here by a Royal Air Force aircraft (complete with inflight-refuelling probe).

Inside the AC-130

Even at night-time the impressive array of sensors and avionics on board this flying gunship can detect and identify unfortunate enemy vehicles in the jungle below, directing awesome firepower from the port side of the aircraft.

The C-130's versatility is legendary, and even ice and snowfields present no problem when it is fitted with a ski undercarriage. Designated LC-130H, these aircraft are employed on polar support missions.

20-mm cannon
Each of these is a six-barrel rotary M61A1 Vulcan.

Radar
The AN/APN-59B set gives forward-looking moving target information.

Air data probe
This supplies airspeed data for the weapon aiming systems.

Truck detector
The AN/ASD-5 'Black Crow' detects truck ignition motors by passive methods.

Deflector plate
This hinges out into the airstream to offset recoil-induced yaw when the guns are firing.

Stabilised tracking set
This group of instruments includes a laser designator/rangefinder and a low light level television.

Sensor turret
An infra-red sensor is mounted here for weapon aiming at night.

Often it is not possible for a transport to land, and the Hercules has pioneered many other supply techniques to overcome this. Paradropping from the open rear ramp is a favourite, dropping anything from sticks of troops to palletised cargo. For bulky cargo such as vehicles, the LAPES (low altitude parachute extraction system) is used: the Hercules flies literally a couple of metres from the ground, and the cargo is pulled out of the back by large parachutes. Mounted on a pallet, it falls to the ground and skids to a stop, causing no damage.

Worldwide use

Immediately after entering service with the US Air Force it was obvious that the C-130 was a winner, and over the years nearly 60 countries have found it the perfect answer to their tactical transport needs, resulting in nearly 2,000 aircraft being manufactured.

All the major Western nations, with the exception of France and West Germany, use the type, and it has found favour with many in the Third World, where its ruggedness and performance are admirably suited to operations from primitive airfields.

The US Air Force is by far the largest user, and its aircraft are a common sight throughout Europe, the Middle East and Far East. Royal Air Force transport squadrons rely heavily on the Hercules, of which some have been stretched to allow them to carry even greater loads for only a small loss of performance.

Throughout its history, the Hercules' simple construction and huge internal volume have made it a natural for conversion. The number of tasks carried out at one time or another almost equals the array of nations that operate the type. C-130s have seen use as bombers, with bombs and even mines being simply rolled out of the open rear door.

Led by the US Marine Corps, several nations have used the type for inflight-refuelling, with either hose-drum units on the wings or in the rear fuselage. Under the designation LC-130, US Navy Hercules have been fitted with skis to support Antarctic operations, the aircraft finding no problem with operating from flat snow and in freezing conditions.

A large array of electronic variants has been produced over the years, including the RC-130 and EC-130E 'Coronet Solo' electronic reconnaissance platforms, the EC-130H countermeasures aircraft and the

Below: The worldwide Hercules fleet is huge, with the US Air Force naturally the largest user. It currently employs over 500 machines.

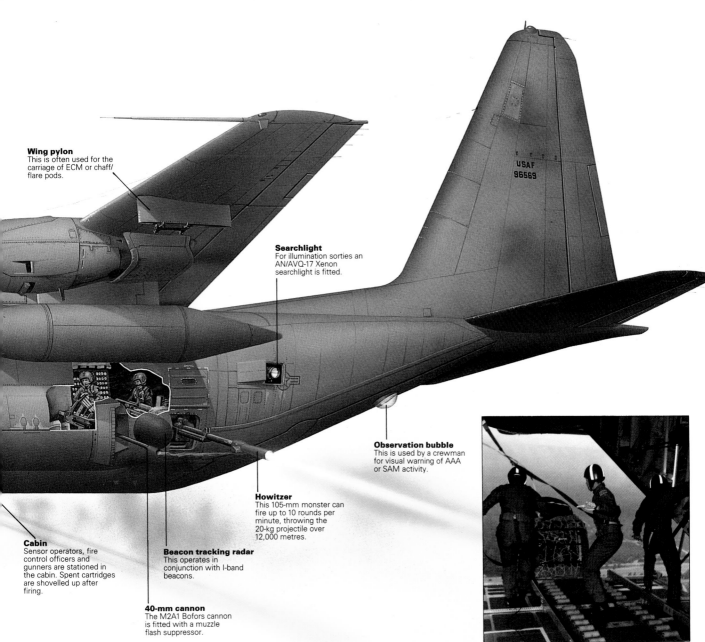

Wing pylon
This is often used for the carriage of ECM or chaff/flare pods.

Searchlight
For illumination sorties an AN/AVQ-17 Xenon searchlight is fitted.

USAF
96569

Observation bubble
This is used by a crewman for visual warning of AAA or SAM activity.

Cabin
Sensor operators, fire control officers and gunners are stationed in the cabin. Spent cartridges are shovelled up after firing.

Howitzer
This 105-mm monster can fire up to 10 rounds per minute, throwing the 20-kg projectile over 12,000 metres.

Beacon tracking radar
This operates in conjunction with I-band beacons.

40-mm cannon
The M2A1 Bofors cannon is fitted with a muzzle flash suppressor.

EC-130E and EC-130Q radio relay/airborne command post modifications. The WC-130 and RAF Hercules W.Mk 2 carry out weather reconnaissance, while various versions of HC-130 perform search and rescue missions, some involving the unique capability of refuelling helicopters in flight.

Support and gunfire

Of course there are many others, such as the DC-130 drone-carrier and a large number of special one-off test aircraft, all going to prove the unmatched versatility of the Hercules. Two more specialist versions deserve further mention, however: the MC-130 and AC-130.

Special Forces' support is the name of the game for the MC-130 'Combat Talon', and it has terrain-avoidance radar to help it perform this task. Low-level flying at night across enemy lines is its chief function, using these missions to drop, supply and extract

Safety-strapped RAF crewmen roll a parachute-retarded container from the open rear ramp of their Hercules.

covert forces. The most experienced pilots are required for this job, as flying in terrible weather through mountains at night is not for the inexperienced.

On the nose of the MC-130 are two extendable forks for the Fulton recovery system. This remarkable device allows agents and equipment to be extracted from difficult terrain, the forks snagging a balloon sent aloft from the ground attached to a cable. Tied to the other end of the cable is the agent or equipment, which is snatched into the air when the balloon is snagged. The Hercules flies off, and the recovered item or agent is hauled in through the rear ramp.

Most spectacular of the Hercules variants is the AC-130 gunship. Used by Special Forces for fire support, interdiction and counter-insurgency,

'Combat Talon' MC-130s are stationed in Germany, the Philippines and the US for Special Forces support. Little is known of their clandestine missions.

this version features a mammoth arsenal of guns protruding from the port side of the aircraft.

Flying in a left-hand orbit around the target, sensors such as imaging infra-red, moving target radar, night vision scopes and truck ignition detectors help the onboard computer aim the weapons, followed by a withering hail of fire upon the often unsuspecting victim.

Deadly weapons

Two versions are currently in use: the AC-130A with two 7.62-mm rotary guns, two 20-mm rotary cannon and two 40-mm cannon; and the AC-130H, which gives up the 7.62-mm weapons

Battlefield Evaluation: comparing

Lockheed C-130 Hercules

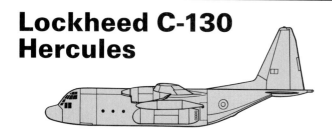

What can be said about the Hercules? In service with nearly 60 nations, and the pioneer of modern tactical assault, the Lockheed C-130 is regarded as one of the world's most important military aircraft, and performs its role so well that, even after over 30 years in service, there is no replacement in sight.

Specification:
Length overall: 29.79 m
Wing span: 40.41 m
Maximum speed: 325 kts
Maximum range: (with maximum payload) 3791 km
Maximum load: 19356 kg
Take-off distance: 1091 m

Assessment
Manoeuvrability	★★★★
Rough field capability	★★★★★
Versatility	★★★★★
Robustness	★★★★★
Worldwide users	★★★★★

The success of the Hercules design has led to a myriad of variants. This is an HC-130 combat rescue aircraft.

Lockheed C-141 StarLifter

The much larger StarLifter, the Hercules' big brother, is used more for long-range transport, but a measure of rough field performance allows its use on some theatre missions. Its main asset is its speed, which allows it to make rapid long-distance flights at little notice.

Specification:
Length overall: 51.29 m
Wing span: 48.74 m
Maximum speed: 492 kts
Maximum range: (with maximum payload) 4725 km
Maximum load: 41222 kg
Take-off distance: 1768 m

Assessment
Manoeuvrability	★★
Rough field capability	★★
Versatility	★★
Robustness	★★★
Worldwide users	★★★

The C-141 is an excellent long-range transport also suited to rough landing strips.

Antonov An-12 'Cub'

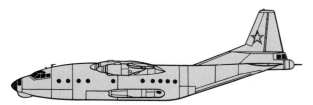

The An-12 is a direct Soviet Hercules equivalent, resembling it in layout as well as role. As with the Hercules, the An-12 has been used for several different roles, such as tactical jamming and electronic reconnaissance. It has been supplied to most Soviet allies and satellite nations.

Specification:
Length overall: 33.10 m
Wing span: 38.00 m
Maximum speed: 419 kts
Maximum range: (with maximum payload) 3600 km
Maximum load: 20000 kg
Take-off distance: 700 m

Assessment
Manoeuvrability	★★★
Rough field capability	★★★★★
Versatility	★★★★
Robustness	★★★★
Worldwide users	★★★★

A direct Soviet competitor to the Hercules, the Antonov An-12 has not matched the Hercules' versatility or robustness.

and one of the 40-mm cannon in favour of a truly massive 105-mm howitzer, enough to spoil even the most ardent guerrilla's night. Although the AC-130 is a fearsome area denial weapon, vehicles and soft installations are its principal fodder.

No end in sight

Amazingly, the Hercules story shows no signs of winding down, with new versions being proposed and production still running. US Special Forces are to receive updated aircraft in the form of the MC-130H and the completely revised AC-130U gunship, while the immense worldwide transport fleet shows no signs of ageing.

Rocket-assisted take-off gear augments the C-130's sprightly performance. This particular machine supports the US Navy's 'Blue Angels' display team.

the C-130 Hercules with its rivals

Ilyushin Il-76 'Candid'

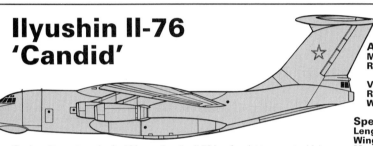

Designed to replace the An-12 in service, the Il-76 is a four-jet transport which combines the advantages of a rough field transport with the speed of jets. Used widely in Afghanistan, the Il-76 is fitted with an array of countermeasures such as decoy flares to deter attacks from the ground. It appears to not be as manoeuvrable as either An-12 or C-130.

Assessment
Manoeuvrability ★★★
Rough field
  capability ★★★★
Versatility ★★
Robustness ★★★
Worldwide users ★★★

Specification:
Length overall: 46.59 m
Wing span: 50.50 m
Maximum speed: 459 kts
Maximum range: (with maximum payload) 5000 km
Maximum load: 48000 kg
Take-off distance: 850 m

'Candid' is a fast and capable rough-field transport, and is steadily replacing the 'Cub' in Soviet service.

Transall C-160

France and West Germany elected to 'go it alone' in terms of a tactical transport, building the C-160 jointly rather than buying Hercules. Although slightly smaller, the Transall fills the role admirably. In French service, it has recently adopted the inflight-refuelling, electronic reconnaissance and radio relay roles.

Specification:
Length overall: 32.40 m
Wing span: 40.00 m
Maximum speed: 277 kts
Maximum range: (with maximum payload) 1850 km
Maximum load: 16000 kg
Take-off distance: 715 m

Assessment
Manoeuvrability ★★★★
Rough field
  capability ★★★★★
Versatility ★★★
Robustness ★★★
Worldwide users ★★

France (illustrated), West Germany, South Africa and Turkey operate the Transall on Hercules-style missions.

Aeritalia G222

To complement its Hercules fleet, Italy builds the G222 as a small tactical transport with even better short field performance. Another main attribute is the type's agility, which is phenomenal for a transport. Overseas sales have been made to several nations, and a number of roles such as reconnaissance, navaid calibration and firefighting have been adopted.

Specification:
Length overall: 22.70 m
Wing span: 28.70 m
Maximum speed: 291 kts
Maximum range: (with maximum payload) 1370 km
Maximum load: 9000 kg
Take-off distance: 662 m

Assessment
Manoeuvrability ★★★★★
Rough field
  capability ★★★★★
Versatility ★★
Robustness ★★★★
Worldwide users ★★★

What the G222 lacks in size and cargo load, it makes up for in short-field performance and manoeuvrability.

THE PRISONER

A prisoner-of-war camp can be anything from a huge barbed wire compound holding tens of thousands of men to a crude shelter in a jungle clearing and one or two men in a bamboo cage. Once your interrogation is over you're of very little use to the enemy, unless he can exploit you for political purposes.

You're just a drain on his resources. The men he has to use to guard you, the food and medicines he has to send to keep you alive: all of these could be better used on the battlefield. So it's going to be tough. The US Government has spent a great deal of time and money to find out what gives its soldiers the best possible chance of getting through a period spent as a PoW. US Army Field Manuals 21-76 and 21-78 are the source for this section on life as a prisoner of war.

Strength through unity

No matter how few of you there are, you must have an organisation. One man must be in command. Chances are that your captors will try to force someone of their choice on you.

If they try to set up an organisation amongst the prisoners, then the best thing to do is to appear to go along. But you'll know who really is the Senior Ranking Officer. He, not the enemy's puppet, will appoint his Adjutant, his Quartermaster, his Welfare, Education and Entertainments Officers and set up rest of the PoW infrastructure.

Eat the food

You will get less, worse and stranger food than you ever had – a poor version of the stuff the enemy eats. If you are a finicky eater, get over it. Many men have died in a short period of captivity because they could not adapt to the food – they have starved themselves to death.

Add to your diet with roots, weeds, bark, a hidden garden, animals or reptiles. Ants and grasshoppers are good sources of protein. Cat, dog and monkey meats are staples of many diets.

Steal from your captors. If your Senior Ranking Officer approves, trade with the enemy, and share with those PoWs who need it at least as much as you do. If it's edible, eat it.

The enemy knows that lack of enough food or the right kinds of food decreases mental and physical powers, making you less able to resist and

The enemy will try to break the morale of all the prisoners: you must try to organise against this. You have an important role in maintaining the morale of your fellow captives.

easier to manipulate. Therefore he will withhold food to make you do what he wants.

Drink the water

You must drink, even though your water smells bad, is dirty and is alive with bugs. Strain or purify it with chemicals or by boiling if you can. Make a still to obtain water, or suck the juices from fruits. Tomatoes are an excellent source of fluid, as are some wild plants such as cacti. Catch rain or snow. If you think, you'll drink; if you panic, you'll dehydrate.

Exercise for survival

Try to take some sort of exercise every day. Keep up your muscle tone, but don't overdo it – you won't be getting the proteins and carbohydrates in your diet that will allow you to do strenuous exercise.

Keep your mind active, too. Try to be learning something new all the time. If you're in a large camp, with lots of other people, the chances are that you'll be able to learn pretty much anything you can think of. You'll have skills that others will want to learn, too.

Play can be just as important as

Inside the forbidding interior of the notorious 'Hanoi Hilton' – the old French prison where many captured US personnel were held by the North Vietnamese.

American prisoners look out at North Vietnamese guards in Hanoi. Give each guard an insulting nickname to use amongst yourselves: it'll make you feel much better.

work. Not just physical games and sports, though these are very important, but entertainments of all kinds. Painting and drawing and writing need very little in the way of materials, and they don't just keep you busy – they allow you to express yourself, your inner thoughts, in an important way.

Remember, it may be hard work trying to stay fit and healthy, but it's nothing compared with the job you've got if you lose your health and fitness and then have to get it back again. Your captors will like it a lot better if you just sit around doing nothing all day and every day, weakening your own morale and destroying your will to stay awake and alive. Don't do it! Your life is in your own hands.

Join in

The men appointed to the jobs of Sports, Education and Entertainments Officers will want to set up as many activities and events as they can. Get involved in these activities. It doesn't matter if you're not too

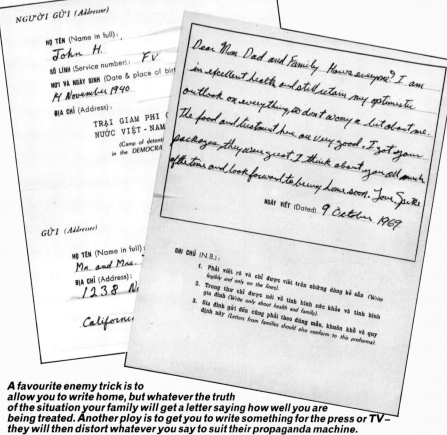

A favourite enemy trick is to allow you to write home, but whatever the truth of the situation your family will get a letter saying how well you are being treated. Another ploy is to get you to write something for the press or TV – they will then distort whatever you say to suit their propaganda machine.

good at whatever it is – what matters most is that you get busy and active and stay that way.

The folks back home

Keeping in touch with your family and friends is very important for both sides. You need to know you're not forgotten and they need to know that you're as safe and well as possible.

Letters and photographs are the only way you'll be able to keep in contact, and the enemy will know this and use it to weaken you. Be ready to share your letters, photographs and parcels, if you get them, with the people around you. The SRO will put someone in charge of mail, and keep an accurate list of letters sent and received.

Outgoing letters are often a source of intelligence for the enemy. Try to restrict yourself to a brief note like, "I'm alive and well," and if you're in any doubt about the value to the enemy of something you want to say in a letter home, ask the SRO's advice – that's another one of the many things he's there for.

Make sure that you circulate any scraps of news that you get in your letters. The best way is for a group of people to produce a camp newspaper. It needn't be more than hand-written sheets that get passed on from person to person around the camp. If that's not possible, then you'll have to do it by word of mouth.

Get one over

Let no chance go by to 'get one over' on the enemy, and make sure that everyone knows about every little victory. Give all the guards and camp personal nick-names – the crueller the better! Don't use them to their faces, of course, but in private use every chance you have to make fun of them. Leave them in no doubt of what you think of them.

Camp communication

There are many ways to communicate with other prisoners. The PoW isolation barrier and enemy-imposed ban on communication must be broken. If you can see, hear or touch other PoWs, or if articles are brought into and taken out of your place of confinement, you can communicate.

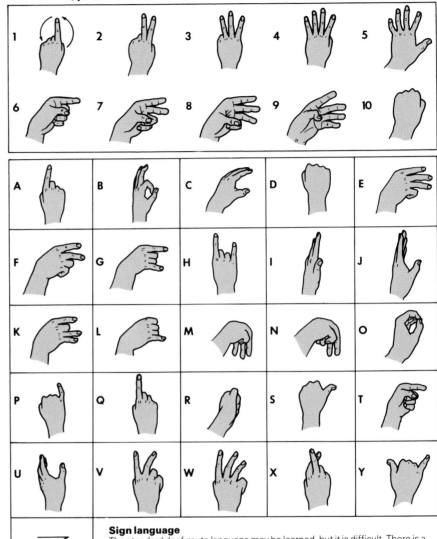

Sign language

The standard deaf-mute language may be learned, but it is difficult. There is a simple variation that is quicker to learn, using hand signals. Either hand can be used. Numbers are rotated to indicate that they are numbers and not letters. The code uses the standard US Navy hand signal numbers; zero is shown by rotating the letter O. Let your hand drop slightly after each series of letters or words.

To indicate 'I understand' or 'I do not understand', the receiver may nod slightly in a prearranged manner. Different body movements such as blinking the eyes, flexing the hands or arms, shrugging the shoulders etc – all natural and meaningless to the enemy – can be worked out in advance to indicate different responses.

Tap codes

The Morse code can be learned quickly. But it has a serious drawback: it consists of dots and dashes that sometimes cannot be distinguished. There is a better system that consists of a square marked off in 25 subsquares; 5 across and 5 up and down, with the letters of the alphabet in the subsquares (the letter K is not used because it sounds like C). The squares running from left to right are rows; the squares from top to bottom are columns.

Taps are used to identify letters. The first series of taps gives the row; after a short pause, the second series of taps gives the column. The letter is in the block where the row and column meet. To find the letter O, for example, three taps would designate the third row (L-M-N-O-P); a slight pause followed by four taps would designate the fourth column (D-I-O-T-Y); the row and column meet at the letter O.

A longer pause indicates the end of a word. Two taps indicate that the word has been received. A series of rapid taps indicates that the word was not received, i.e. not understood. When a receiver has enough letters to know what the word is, he gives two taps and the sender goes on to the next word. Each time the code is broken by your captors, you can rearrange the letters.

The methods of getting a message across with this code are almost unlimited. The code can be tapped, whistled, winked, coughed, sneezed or hummed; you can nudge the guy next to you; you can use finger movements, eye movements, twitches, broom strokes, pushups; or you can bang objects together.

2. Then tap these columns.

1. Tap these rows first.

	1	2	3	4	5
1	A	B	C K	D	E
2	F	G	H	I	J
3	L	M	N	O	P
4	Q	R	S	T	U
5	V	W	X	Y	Z

This is how to tap the message HEADS UP

```
1 2      1 2 3           1       1 2 3 4 5
■ ■      ■ ■ ■  (H)      ■       ■ ■ ■ ■ ■  (E)

1  1          1      1 2 3 4         1 2 3 4     1 2 3
■  ■  (A)     ■      ■ ■ ■ ■  (D)    ■ ■ ■ ■     ■ ■ ■  (S)

1 2 3 4     1 2 3 4 5
■ ■ ■ ■     ■ ■ ■ ■ ■  (U)

1 2 3     1 2 3 4 5
■ ■ ■     ■ ■ ■ ■ ■  (P)
```

Talking through the wall
Roll up a blanket in the shape of a ring doughnut and put it against the wall. Put your face in the centre of the doughnut and talk slowly. The receiver puts his ear against the wall on the other side, or presses the open end of a cup against the wall with his ear against the other end.

Different noises
Various sounds such as grunting, coughing, sneezing, blowing your nose, whistling or humming can be used as prearranged signals to pass messages such as 'all is well', 'enemy around', 'stop', 'go' etc.

Word of mouth
This can sometimes be dangerous. To disguise the content from the enemy, language variations can be used; subculture language (street language of minority groups), for example, or pidgin English, ordinary slang etc.

Writing messages
You will not usually have writing materials available. But you can improvise: use charred wood, fruit juices, ashes mixed with any fluid etc. Use any pointed object as a writing implement. Leaves, wood, cloth, toilet paper and any other material can be used as a writing surface.

Mail deliveries
As well as personal deliveries, messages can be left in any hiding place – latrines, trees, rocks, crevices, holes etc; the best places are those that the enemy would expect you to visit normally. The hiding places should be changed frequently, and couriers should deposit and collect their despatches at different times.

Survival

Escape, Rescue and Release

The best chances to escape will come straight after your capture. You'll still be close to your own forces, and so you'll know which direction to head in, and you may even be familiar with the country. You'll be fitter and healthier than after time spent in captivity, and if you can keep your wits about you, you may be able to take advantage of the confusion that is usually to be found just behind the fighting front, with reinforcements and resupply trying to go forward and medevac and empty resupply units trying to move back.

The first hours

You'll be in the hands of combat troops, not people trained in holding prisoners, and their inexperience may give you opportunities. But at the same time they'll be psyched up for battle, so will probably shoot rather than ask questions. They might just shoot you for the fun of it.

For all these reasons, every army has a plan for dealing with prisoners of war, for getting them out of the combat zone as quickly as possible, so that they can be interrogated while the information they have about troop strengths and movements is still worth something.

The chances are that if you're captured on your own, or as part of a

Take advantage of the confusion associated with your capture. You will be passed between different enemy units and transit camps, and security here is often the weakest.

The possibilities of escape

Escapes are much more likely to succeed if the prisoners are properly organised with an escape committee and a chain of command. It needs many hands to forge documents, create disguises and provide tools for the job. When you make your bid for freedom other prisoners can create a diversion to distract the guards.

The gate
Perhaps the best escape route is through the front gate, hidden in enemy vehicles.

Bluff
You may be able way past the gu disguised as a w remember, you be complete.

On the outside
Outdoor working parties provide the best opportunities for escape: at least you're beyond the camp wire. And you should have a couple of hours clear before the next head-count.

small group, you will be held somewhere like the regimental command post, and then transferred to the rear echelon headquarters run by intelligence security units, military police or internal security troops. This will not be far from the fighting front.

In transit

When enough prisoners have accumulated, you'll be moved back, being kept to open country and avoiding towns and villages. The enemy is likely to be short of motor transport – or, at least, will give a very low priority to the transportation of prisoners, so you may well find yourself evacuated on foot.

He'll be short of personnel, too, so the PoW column may have too few guards, who may even be not fit for active duty – walking wounded perhaps, themselves on their way to rear echelon hospitals. That means that there will be more chances to escape.

If the guards are placed at the head and tail of the column, as is often the case, pass the word through the ranks of prisoners to spread out and make the line of marching men as long as possible.

Keep the pace as slow as you can. At a bend in the road, you may suddenly find that the head and the tail are out of each other's sight, which means that men in the centre of the column can slip away to either side of the road and get quickly into some kind of cover.

The larger the number of men who make a break, the greater are the chances of their absence being noticed straight away. One or two men missing probably won't be noticed until the next head count is made, and that may not be until the end of the day.

Take advantage of any diversion, too. Artillery bombardment and attack from the air or extreme weather conditions, for instance, are likely to cause a lot of confusion, and may permit men to slip away while the guards' attention is distracted.

Road transport

If you're being transported by truck out of the combat zone, you will probably be moved by night. If the guards are not alert and you are not locked inside the vehicle, you may get a chance to jump for it when the truck

Tunnel out
Tunnels are a big undertaking and require an organised team. Getting rid of the spoil is as big a problem as digging the tunnel itself.

Tools
Collect anything that will serve as a tool. If you find a proper tool on a work party out of camp, hide it away for a few days or weeks before smuggling it back in.

Tunnel around
If you can't tunnel out, perhaps you can tunnel from one part of the camp to another – perhaps to a food store or another group of prisoners.

Sleeping dummy
Move your bed into a corner of your cell as far as possible from the guards' view, some weeks before your escape attempt so that they can get used to it. Then put a dummy under your blankets before you go missing.

The wire
There have been many successful attempts at going through the wire, but beware mines and electronic sensors.

Cover
Plan your escape to coincide with rain and bad visibility. Your guards' senses will be less effective in bad weather.

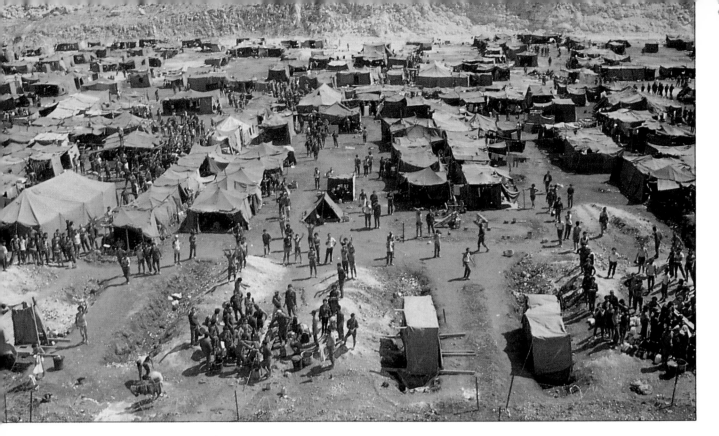

slows down – climbing a hill, for instance, or negotiating a section of damaged road. Try to sabotage the vehicles – put sugar or sand in the petrol, for example – so that they are forced to stop. Once again, an air raid may give you the necessary cover and distraction for an escape attempt.

On the railways

Permanent PoW camps are usually placed as far away as possible from the battlefield and from borders with neutral or enemy territory, so the last move will probably be made by train. Large groups of prisoners in transit are usually locked into freight cars, the guards relying on the physical security of the locked wagons to stop escape attempts.

Ex-PoWs receive a briefing from a reception officer after their release from North Vietnamese prison camps. Many vets were mentally and physically scarred; others didn't make it back at all.

The conditions inside these cars, especially during a long journey in the middle of summer or winter, can become lethal, and the fact that you'll probably be packed in very tightly doesn't help. Even so, because you'll have long periods without observation, this may provide your best chance. Try to break through the floor, the walls (especially at a window or a ventilator), or the roof.

If you're travelling in passenger coaches, then you have two other advantages, even though you may have guards to worry about: it's much easier and quicker to break out through a window than the solid sides of a freight wagon, and you'll probably be able to communicate in some way with prisoners in other compartments or even in other carriages.

Try to create a disturbance to divert the guards' attention; then a whole group may be able to break out and scatter across the countryside. Some, at least, are likely to get far enough away from the immediate vicinity to stand a real chance of getting clean away. One thing to remember – watch out for oncoming trains on adjacent tracks before you jump.

Never start a fire in the van if locked in (as shown in many PoW films) – the guards may respond too slowly.

Don't relax for a moment, but always stay alert to any possibility, because you never know if you'll ever get another chance. If you're not in a position to escape yourself, help others to do so even if it means that you'll be punished for it later.

Temporary camps fairly near the battlefront offer better opportunities for escape than established Prisoner of War camps far behind the lines.

In the camp

Escaping from an established prisoner-of-war camp is a much more difficult task than making a break from a train or from a column of marching men.

The camp itself will have been built specifically to keep you in: barbed wire, electronic surveillence, floodlights, watch towers, dogs and thermal imaging for tunnel searches are just some of the weapons at the enemy's disposal. And even if you do succeed in getting out of the camp itself, you're still faced with a difficult and dangerous journey through enemy territory, where just your physical appearance may be enough to give you away.

The escape committee

Part of the prisoners' secret organization in the camp will be devoted to the business of escaping. There will be very few ways of making an escape from a camp, and each time an attempt is made it will cut down those possibilities even further.

The Escape Committee will coordinate escape attempts, to try to ensure that each one has the best possible chance of success, and also set up the infrastructure that each will need – tools, diversions, false documents, intelligence and so on. You should collect and hoard everything, even useless articles: these will mask the

As technology takes over from human observation and scrutiny, escape has become more and more difficult. But what technology has taken away with one hand it has given back with the other. Spy satellites and high-altitude observation flights give intelligence officers a clear view of every part of the earth's surface. That means you have a way of signalling to your own people, no matter where on earth you may be.

There's no need to rush it. You can trace out the letters of a message in the soil of a compound – or even stand around in groups that shape the letter in such a way that the enemy won't even be aware that you're doing it.

Make certain that each arm of each letter is at least 2 metres long, or it might not be seen from above. But remember, it's as likely to be seen by enemy satellites as your own.

Once your position has been identified – either by this method, or by a successful escaper being de-briefed, a coded letter getting through, or an enemy national selling the information – it may be possible for a rescue mission to be put together. Even if you're four or five hundred miles from the nearest friendly border or sea coast, your own authorities may be able to get a rescue force through.

The odds on a successful rescue will be a lot greater if there's a channel of communication from the would-be rescuers to you, and that probably means coded radio messages. There have been many cases of prisoners building radio receivers in camps, and here technology lends a hand once again, modern radio receivers being small enough to be easily hidden in all sorts of places.

Any information should include a validation code, such as mention of a prearranged subject such as trees or weather, or even the days of the week. Leave this code off only when under duress.

Every piece of information that you can exchange with the people planning the rescue attempt will increase its chances of success. One of the most vital will be to set up the signalling system you'll use to call the rescue force in at the last moment.

The chances are that it will be helicopter-borne, and the pilots and mission commanders will need to be shown exactly where to land to be most effective; wind direction; where to expect resistance; and perhaps even where the prisoners they've come to rescue are to be found.

Be patient, and above all, be secure. A rescue attempt that fails because the enemy have got to know about the plan will not only cost the lives of the rescue force, but also give the enemy a huge propaganda victory.

useful ones if you are searched by camp guards.

Most escape attempts will need this sort of organisation – but that doesn't mean that you shouldn't go for it on your own if a chance presents itself unexpectedly, perhaps from a labour party working outside the camp.

Documents and disguises

Before you get too far in your escape planning, you have to think how you'll cross the enemy territory that lies between you and neutral or friendly forces. There are two methods – either you try to blend in with the local population, or you try to stay hidden.

If you try to fit in, you'll need clothing, documents, money and at least some knowledge of the language, all of which will either have to be produced inside the camp or stolen once you get outside.

In order to forge documents, you have to know what they look like to start with, and you must have the right sort of raw material available – paper,

inks and dyes, pens, and so on, not to mention the skill to do it. And as magnetic encoding like that used on credit cards gets more common, the chances decrease of producing forged documents that will pass any sort of examination.

The other option is to travel in secret, using your survival training to keep out of enemy hands. In many

If you are shot down over enemy territory it may be possible for US aircraft and helicopters to mount a rescue mission. Here a US pilot brought down over North Vietnam managed to maintain contact with US aircraft. He is picked up by helicopter while other US aircraft provide security.

ways this is more practical, and at least you know where you are when you depend only on your own skills.

Improvised signals to aircraft

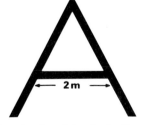

S
O
S

Unless aircraft are flying slowly at low altitude you will probably not be seen. To attract the attention of friendly aircraft you need to make a large sign which will stand out: letters should have arms of not less than two metres.

Alternatively, you can send the emergency 'SOS' signal in Morse code. Look around for any useful material: stones, fertilizer sacks, anything that can be arranged into a shape to catch the pilots' attention. Or, when on parade in POW camp, form your parade up so that it spells out the letters 'SOS' as shown above.

Fighting Fit
THE ROYAL MARINES SNIPER COURSE

A sniper's main aids to observation are the Schmidt und Bender telescopic sight, the Scout Regiment telescope, and the ×6 prismatic binoculars. After the "Mark 1 eyeball", the ×6 are the most useful: they are small, compact and light, and give a relatively wide field of view, enabling a large area to be searched quickly. The lens is marked off with graticules set 10 mils apart, with vertical heights of 20, 10 and 5 mils respectively, which can be used to give angular measurements. The binoculars even have some use in darkness, allowing you to see about four times better than with the naked eye.

There is another piece of equipment specifically for night-time use: the Weapon-sight Image Intensifier, or Individual Weapon Sight (IWS). The IWS enables infantry direct fire weapons to fire by night at targets up to 300 metres away. The sight is battery operated and collects all level light from the area being viewed, which is intensified to produce a clear image of the area.

The IWS consists of a lens with a protective lens hood and light filter, a

On the first day of Week 3 you are paired off to construct a hide, which you will occupy all night as an observation post. This tests your camouflage skill and mental alertness.

Making a Hide

The first stage is clearing the ground where you will dig in: the idea is to be completely concealed with overhead cover. Each pair of would-be snipers makes its hide on the same gorse-covered ridge.

range focussing knob, a battery housing with an on/off switch, an inverter housing, an eyepiece and eye guard, and a universal adaptor. The body of the sight houses an optical arrangement of lenses with phosphor-coated green-tinted screens, resulting in a bright green image visible through the eyepiece.

The IWS can be mounted on the SLR, GPMG, AR15 and 84-mm anti-tank gun (Carl Gustav). The sight has a magnification of ×3.75, focussing

from 10 metres to infinity. It is an indispensible aid to night observation, giving you a tremendous advantage over your adversary, and in the hands of a trained sniper that advantage is much greater.

Constructing a hide: rural OPs

Whenever possible a sniper should work from a hide, since it allows some free movement without the danger of detection and gives some protection from the weather and shrapnel. Individual hides will vary greatly depending on the time available, the shape and type of ground, the proximity of the enemy, and your own ingenuity.

On the first day of course week 3, you are paired off and allocated one of six positions stretching along the crest of a gorse-covered hill. The Army's sniper training pamphlet suggests that when a semi-permanent or permanent hide is required, you will usually need the help of Royal Engineers. But the Royal Marines show you that it *is* possible to construct such a hide without assistance from the Royal Engineers or anyone else. They allow you the luxury of a few building materials: some wooden beams, a metal picket

The digging begins at 1345 hrs, and after a couple of hours' work most hides are excavated down to several feet in depth. Some pairs strike lucky and find the soil easy going, but others are not so fortunate.

man hide in a little less than eight hours! Most of you will.

1345 hrs: You begin clearing the area by digging out turfs, which you stack close by to be used when camming-out. It's hard work, and although a cold wind is blowing you soon discard your heavy ghilly suit top.

1505 hrs: The topsoil has been cleared and you can get on with some serious digging. One lucky pair has a patch of unusually soft earth and is making good progress. The remainder toil away at the hard, pebble-filled soil.

1630 hrs: Most of you are now down about two-thirds of a metre. The pair who had an easy start has now struck an unyielding, clay-like layer and is struggling, but another pair in a nearby position has hit soft earth.

1750 hrs: You're all down to about

for supporting overhead cover, sheets of corrugated iron ("wriggly tin"), and a few sandbags. In place of the RE's plastic explosive, you get picks and shovels.

A senior instructor briefs each pair on their arcs of fire, of vital importance when siting the loopholes. He rounds off his instruction with:

"Make sure you're in position by 0530 hours".

This allows you a generous 16 hours to clear the ground, dig a pit (taking care to conceal the spoil), conceal the pit with overhead cover and, finally, camouflage the position and immediate area. Unofficially, however, you're expected to complete the two-

So you thought sniping was all glamour! The afternoon turns into a heavy slog as you struggle to get the hide finished by last light.

Some pairs decide to take it by turns towards the end of the afternoon. You must finish the digging well before dusk to camouflage the hide properly.

By 1930 hrs you are up to your elbows, and the actual pit is pretty well complete. You are also tired and not in the best condition for an all-night vigil.

the same depth – a metre or so. After four hours you decide to take it in turns, one man digging for a few minutes at a time while the other takes a short rest.

1930 hrs: You've nearly finished the pit. It will be an hour or two before the overhead cover is in place and cammed out, but you've made remarkably good progress. By the time the sun is setting behind the hills on your right, you're ready to move into your hide. The final touches to the camouflage will be added at first light.

0700 hrs: When the senior instructor inspects the positions, he is quietly satisfied with what he sees – or doesn't see! He chats with the occupants of each pit, advising them on how to improve their hide and on how to add to the camouflage. Almost without exception, the snipers have left too much of the loopholes exposed. It's surprising how much difference a few sprigs of gorse can make.

You spend the rest of the morning observing the area to the front of your positions. A number of Royal Marines, dressed in Soviet uniform, provide you with an occasional incident to record in your logs. It's a long, tedious period, and very little happens. The exercise is intended to teach you patience and perseverance: if you can't stand a few hours, you won't last days or even weeks in a genuine operational situation. An instructor explains:

"Sometimes we have to fail a person for something when he might otherwise have made a good sniper. On the other hand, there are a minority who get through who might not have quite the right temperament suited to the job. This might not become evident

Getting the overhead cover on properly takes longer than you anticipated. Here one pair get the wriggly tin in place with two hours to go before dusk.

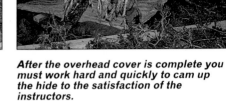

After the overhead cover is complete you must work hard and quickly to cam up the hide to the satisfaction of the instructors.

until much later, when the guy is on active service. Then you might have to share an OP with someone for days on end, remain quiet and observant, and not crack the other bloke up. Extroverts usually do not make ideal snipers. A sniper tends to be something of an introvert."

Urban OPs

In urban areas, a study of large-scale street maps, sewer plans, low-level oblique photographs and street photography provided by patrols will help to show the general areas suitable for hides. Once these have been established, you can carry out further ground reconnaissance to plan the approach route, entry and exit point and arcs of observation.

A secure and quiet approach with the minimum number of obstacles such as dustbins, crumbling walls and barking dogs is ideal. You may need a diversion in the form of a VCP or house search so that you can use the cover of a vehicle to approach the area unseen and occupy the hide.

Buildings can often offer good opportunities as sniping posts, but they also run the risk of attracting the attention of the enemy's heavier weapons. Isolated houses may well be singled out even if you have not been detected.

In unconventional situations such as Northern Ireland, there are extra considerations when selecting a building for use as an OP. It's no use positioning a pair of snipers behind a first-floor window on the same route as a half-hourly double-decker bus. And there's no point inserting an OP on a third-level landing if the area to be observed is the street below. Use your training and common sense when called upon to construct a hide, whether it is in the countryside or a built-up area. Follow the rules and you shouldn't be compromised.

On the ridge seen below are six hides dug in: potentially a dozen crack shots with sniper rifles, and you can't see a thing. Inset: the view from an observation loophole in a hide.

Combat Report
Rhodesia:
Anti-Guerrilla Patrol

Taking aim with the FN FAL, an excellent weapon that outranged the enemy AK-47s. Anyone hit by 7.62-mm NATO ammo tended to stay down.

A soldier who fought in the Rhodesian Army describes how his OP discovered a guerrilla unit in a village near the border with Mozambique.

During the early months of 1977 I was serving in the Eastern Highlands of Rhodesia, not far from the Mozambique border. It was reputed to be one of the more picturesque areas in the country: a touch of the Scottish Highlands in the heart of Africa.

I was Two One Charlie's Bren gunner. Our Stick Leader was Corporal David Smith, otherwise known as Smiddy. The other two were Andy Krapper and 'Boom'; I can't remember his real name.

We'd been out for three days and nights, showing a presence in the area. We knew that Charlie Tango were about, but they weren't interested in a direct confrontation; they were engaged in winning the sympathies of the indigenous population.

The fourth day was much the same as the other three. The rain hadn't let up for a moment, and the going was painfully slow as our weight pushed us into the clinging mud. The streams were brown swirling torrents.

It was starting to get dark, but we hadn't yet moved into our night position. Smiddy was on the set to our relay station, sending the daily situation report back to platoon HQ. He was scribbing something on his OS map and signalled for us to come close. HQ had received information that a Charlie Tango band had regular feeding at a village about 15 km east of us, and we were to check it out.

Night was soon upon us

According to the map, the village was out in the middle of cultivated land with only sparse bush and a few granite outcrops nearby. With such poor cover we had no option but to try to move into an OP position under cover of darkness. We were confident that we could cover the 15 km within four or five hours, so off we went.

Night was soon upon us. What a night it was: the continuous drizzle developed into a heavy downpour, and it was pitch black. The wind had

In this village the Charlie Tangos were present in strength. Unfortunately more villagers than guerrillas were killed.

also picked up, and was hurling the rain at us in solid sheets. It was terrible. As we pressed on, my mind started to drift into oblivion. It was about two in the morning. Suddenly a dog started barking and I was back to reality.

We stopped immediately, instinctively crouching and remaining motionless until the barking stopped. Talk about a fluke: we had walked right into the village we were looking for. We retraced our steps for a good 50 metres before stopping to plan our next move.

One carried the lethal RPD

We began to circle the village in the hope of finding an outcrop with enough cover to conceal us and serve as an OP. By five o'clock none of the positions we had checked were ideal, but with daylight approaching we crawled into the best we could find. Smiddy took the first watch.

I was awoken by Krapper prodding me with the binoculars. It was nine o'clock. The rain was still coming down, but gently. The village lay about 150 metres to our front. Smoke was seeping out of the thatch of a dozen or so huts; in all I counted about 40.

The day passed but was pretty uneventful, and I was feeling a bit depressed. To make matters worse, Krapper came down with a bout of gastroenteritis; it was sheer hell for all of us. We were glad when darkness came and Smiddy ordered him to take his mess tin, exhume it all and re-bury it 20 metres downwind.

The rest of the night passed slowly. Nobody slept. In the early hours the rain stopped and the stars began to appear. Soon the eastern horizon was silhouetted against an ever-growing golden orange background. The stars faded away, and the once black sky rapidly changed through every conceivable shade of blue.

Day Six had begun, and again there was nothing to report. Just before sunset Smiddy sent our sitrep to platoon HQ and was told we were being picked up in the morning by truck at nine o'clock. Hot water, clean clothes and cold beer: now I had something to look forward to.

Morning came at last. At about twenty to nine we heard the rumble of Bedford engines. I was on my knees knocking some of the caked mud off my jacket when Smiddy snapped at me to get down. All his attention was on the village: evidently we weren't the only ones to hear the vehicles. People were running in all directions, herding children into the huts.

Smiddy got on the set to our platoon commander, who had accompanied the trucks. Obviously they couldn't pick us up, and they couldn't just turn round now that they had been heard. The new plan was for them to arrive and pretend to enquire about another village that they had in fact just passed. They would then de-bus and come back. It would work; they already thought we were stupid.

The trucks pulled up outside the village store and the commander walked, map in hand, up to a group of the village elders who were squatting about 20 metres away. Three or four of them jumped up and pointed in the direction the trucks had come from. The trucks turned round and headed back, with everyone waving goodbye.

Within minutes, the villagers re-appeared. Then eight heavily-armed Charlie Tangos casually emerged from a bushy outcrop at the far side of the village. One carried the lethal RPD – a drum-fed machine-gun – and another the mortar tube, and the others had AK-47 assault rifles.

Smiddy radioed the escort sticks; they were

well on their way back and would be with us in 15 minutes. The locals were giving the Charlie Tangos a heroes' welcome.

We checked our webbing, ammunition and weapons. My stomach was screwed up, my mouth was dry, and I was sweating like a pig. The escort sticks radioed that they were ready.

We emerged from cover, splitting up our extended line formation to at least 20 metres apart. The other sticks did the same. We were under orders from the commander not to fire until he did; the idea was to try to cover as much open ground as possible before being detected. By now my nerves were electric. We were in plain view of anyone who cared to look up. When the hell would the commander fire? As if in answer, the sound of machine-gun and rifle fire filled the air.

I was totally shattered

The scene at the store was instantly chaotic. The mass of people seemed to explode like a bomb, running in all directions. Women and children were screaming. Charlie Tango didn't seem to know where the fire was coming from; some ran into huts with the locals, but others were running blindly out of the village.

I found myself running on course with one of them. I fired a short burst at him with my gun still at waist level. He carried on. I stopped and put the LMG to my shoulder and fired another shaky but aimed burst, emptying my magazine. He carried on.

A crazed fear gripped me. I went to ground, ripping off the empty magazine and replacing it with a charged one. He had seen me now, and was about 15 to 20 paces away, shooting at me with a pistol. I could hear the air rip as his bullets passed above me.

He was so close now that I hardly needed to aim. My finger remained on the trigger until the magazine was empty. It was one of the most horrific moments of my life. I watched his face contorting, his body shuddering as my bullets found their mark. He was behind me when he finally crumpled. He was quite dead, but terror still showed on his grey, disfigured face.

I was totally shattered. I began to run towards the village and joined up with Smiddy. Dead and wounded were everywhere. Huts were burning, children were crying, and the wounded were whimpering. The air was strong with the stench of cordite, mixed with burning thatch.

We began sweeping the entire area and had soon accounted for all eight Charlie Tangos. Twenty-three locals had perished, and many more had been wounded. Before leaving, I went to have a last look at the dead Charlie Tango who had refused to fall and whose face is firmly engraved on my memory.

Fighting Fit

THE ROYAL MARINES SNIPER COURSE

Perfecting the Sniper's Technique

It takes weeks of intensive training and practice to be able to shoot a high score consistently. Your specialised sniper training will start very early on in basic training. Later, when you're posted to your unit, your proficiency will be kept up by frequent sessions on the firing range.

During each of the first three weeks of the sniper's training course, at least one day is devoted to live firing. The fourth and last week is given over almost entirely to range work, four days and a night being spent on Okehampton or Willsworthy Ranges on Dartmoor. By the end of that week, your shooting skills will have reached a peak.

Good shooting is good shooting, whether your weapon is the SA80 or a purpose-built sniper's rifle. The essential skills become automatic, but not by themselves. You have to work hard to perfect your skill at arms to the point where good, accurate shooting becomes effortless.

The L96 (Model PM "Infantry") rifle

The British Armed Forces are now phasing out the 7.62-mm L42A1 sniper rifle in favour of the new 7.62-mm L96 A1 Model PM infantry rifle. The L96 PM Infantry measures 1124mm-1194mm with a width of 90mm, and weighs 6.5kgs (as compared to the L42's 4.53kgs). It is equipped with a removable two-stage

Sniper firing positions

Which firing position you adopt when in action will obviously depend on the tactical situation. Here an instructor demonstrates some of the firing positions in which you must become proficient. All have the same purpose: to provide as solid a firing platform as possible while offering a small target to the enemy.

Laid back with sling over knee

Prone, using the bipod

Practice on the Willsworthy ranges, Dartmoor. One sniper fires his L96 while his number 2 observes the fall of shot. Most of your firing sessions take place during the day, but there is a night shoot later in the week.

Firing at up to 1,000 metres, you rely on the Schmidt & Bender PM 6×42 telescopic sight. Iron sights are fitted in case there is a problem with the optics.

Almost all of the fourth week of the sniper course is devoted to shooting. All your stalking and camouflage skills will be no use unless you can shoot with consistent accuracy. The L96 sniper rifle is a superbly accurate weapon: your job is to introduce as little human error as possible.

interchangeable trigger, adjusted to operate on a 4 lbs pull – the minimum weight permitted by HM Government. Like the L42, the L96 is fitted with a 10 round detachable box magazine, which can also be hand fed through the loading port. The weapon is designed to operate at up to 1000 m and is fitted with the Schmidt und Bender PM 6 × 42 telescopic sight. An iron sight is also supplied as an auxiliary sighting system.

The stock is constructed from a tough plastic material finished in "olive drab". There is a detachable ball-mounted bipod on the muzzle end of the chassis with each leg independently adjustable for length by up to 110mm. The bipod allows horizontal rotation to facilitate target tracking, while its ball mount allows up to 10 degrees of cant.

Holding, firing and trigger control

The essentials of good shooting are similar whatever rifle you are using.

(a) A comfortable fire position

(b) Maintaining a firm hold with the trigger hand

(c) Correct alignment of the sights with the target

(d) Firing without disturbing the aim

With the bolt action L96, the basic firing positions and hold are similar to those used when firing a semi-automatic rifle. There is no pistol grip, however, so the right hand must grip the small of the butt. In the prone position your body should be as far round to the left of the line of fire as is possible without the bolt touching your cheek on reloading.

The single most important aspect of marksmanship is the ability to squeeze the trigger without disturbing your aim! A firm right-hand grip is essential. A loose grip tightens up as the trigger is squeezed, so that you lose control. Hold the rifle so the foresight does not move at the moment of

Hawkins position

Modified Hawkins

Single Point Sling

firing. The sniper rifle trigger has two distinct pressures. Take up the first as you begin to aim. As you perfect it, apply a steadily increasing pressure to take up the second. Simultaneously, concentrate on perfecting the aim picture so that it coincides with the shot. Practice trigger control again and again, until it becomes a conditioned reflex.

Faults in techniques

It is important that you are comfortable when firing, and that your rifle fits you. (The rubber buttpad of the L96 is manufactured with removable dovetailed plastic spaces for length adjustment). Make sure that your elbows are spaced a comfortable distance apart to reduce lateral instability. Both hands should grip the weapon so as to avoid strain, as this leads to unsteadiness and will quickly tire you. Your telescopic sight emphasises any wobble. Don't fight it. Come off the aim, relax, and then try again.

No-one can fire a rifle without introducing some element of human error. You must learn about these errors and their effects in order to minimise them. Inadequate instruction, lack of practice, lack of determination or unfitness can result in an unsteady fire position, causing wobble and poor shooting. Training and practice will reduce this movement to a minimum.

Successful precision shooting only comes with dedicated practice. Fired from a clamp, your rifle achieves pinpoint accuracy. Only a relaxed and steady firing position will allow you to follow suit.

Intensive coaching from the instructors helps everyone improve their shooting. You are learning from some of the best rifle shots in the world.

Anticipating the shock of discharge sometimes causes the rifleman to flinch, a reflex action which will seriously affect your shooting. One method of detecting this is to fire a weapon loaded with a mixture of ball and drill ammunition. As long as you don't know when a drill round is fed, flinching can clearly be seen in anticipation of a discharge that fails to occur. If you are affected by flinching, realising the cause of the problem is the first step towards solving it.

Not being able to operate the trigger smoothly and firmly will also result in poor shooting. A loose grip with the trigger hand may well cause you to "snatch" at the trigger, so that the shot falls low and right. Quick and smooth trigger action is essential. The longer you remain in the aim, the more you will tire. Ideal trigger leverage is obtained if the trigger is squeezed low down using the middle of the finger rather than the tip, to minimise the effect of drag when applying the second pressure. A good test of smooth trigger operation is to balance a small coin on the muzzle of your rifle to see if it stays there while you fire a dry shot.

Finally, be sure that when firing you breathe correctly. Breathe in deeply, exhale, breathe in slowly, exhale and hold it. Ensure your sight picture is correct, and fire. Relax and breathe normally.

Fire positions

A sniper often has to improvise a firing position to suit a particular situation. Before you can do this you need to revise the positions you learned during basic training. The exceptions are the Hawkins and Back Positions.

The Hawkins Position can be used when firing from a very low bank or fold in the ground. You lie on your front, keeping as low to the ground as possible, and much more to the left than usual. The left forearm rests on the ground for the greater part of its length while the left hand, clenching the upper sling swivel, maintains a forward pressure to control recoil on firing. The toe of the butt rests on the ground under your shoulder.

Depending on the ground, you may not be able to get enough muzzle depression while in the Hawkins Position. To remedy this, place the butt on the point of your shoulder or upper arm.

The Back Position is useful for firing down slopes. You lie on your back with the rifle butt in your shoulder and the left hand steadying the butt with an overhand grip. By crossing your legs you can rest the rifle on your left thigh. Changing the position of your legs provides for muzzle elevation and depression. To get a satisfactory sight picture you need to keep your head still. You can rest it on the front of available cover or on your telescope case.

The Sitting, Kneeling, Kneeling Supported, Standing and Standing Supported positions are the same as those taught during basic training. You need only modify these positions to suit your own requirements.

Sniper positions (continued)

Double Point Sling

Forward sling swivel brace

Combat Report
Borneo:
Jungle Reconnaissance

Michael Dewar commanded a platoon in Borneo in 1965 when Indonesian troops were threatening the former British colonies along their border. Here he tells the story of a reconnaissance patrol in the jungle.

I arrived in Borneo with my battalion, The Rifle Brigade, in the summer of 1965, commanding the 28-man No. 5 Platoon of B Company. The Borneo War had been going on for over two years; President Sukarno of Indonesia had vowed to crush the emergent federation of Malaysia, which included the former British colonies of Sabah and Sarawak, and with which Indonesian Borneo or Kalimantan shared a border. The British government had deployed the British Army there to ensure that this did not happen.

Vast mountain ranges dominate the island of Borneo. These are interspersed with valleys and plateaux, all of which are covered by tropical rain forest. The 100-ft trees cast a deep green gloom. The streams are infested with leeches (I once burnt 17 off various parts of my anatomy with a lighted cigarette). The hillsides are sometimes almost vertical. A pair of canvas jungle boots rots after two weeks.

A game of cat and mouse

In the lowland swamp areas of western Borneo, the nights are nearly as hot as the days. Elsewhere in the highlands, where I was operating with my platoon, the night air was so cold that we shivered in our jungle green uniforms even inside a sleeping bag.

Our 'fort' at Gunan Gajak, from which we would carry out patrols of usually 10 to 12 days, was built on high ground about three miles from the border with Indonesia. It was surrounded by

Jungle boots only lasted a couple of weeks in the lowland swamp areas of Borneo and the streams were full of leeches. The wear and tear on both men and equipment was severe.

a perimeter of barbed wire and 'punjis' – sturdy fire-hardened bamboo sticks sharpened at both ends and driven into the ground at a 45-degree angle, presenting a would-be attacker with a needle-sharp array at thigh height, upon which he would hopefully impale himself.

Between patrols, there would be respites of three or four days, which were spent getting rid of the grime and dirt, removing a 10 day growth of beard, drawing new clothing and equipment, and cleaning and checking personal weapons for the next patrol.

Patrolling was a strain. An encounter with the enemy was often unplanned, unexpected and fleeting in nature. The perpetual dilemma of a patrol commander was whether to follow a track and risk walking into an ambush or treading on an anti-personnel mine, or to hack his way through almost impenetrable secondary jungle at the rate of perhaps 200 yards an hour. Inevitably, risks had to be taken or the jungle could never have been dominated. It was a game of cat and mouse, of hide and seek, and sometimes even of bluff and counter-bluff.

It was on one such patrol that one of my riflemen lost his leg. My platoon was tasked with carrying out a close reconnaissance on an Indonesian kampong (village) to find out if there were any Indonesian troops based there. The kampong was about 12 miles away through mountainous jungle, and it took nearly three days to get there.

On the evening of the third day I led the platoon into an area of thick jungle a few hundred yards from the enemy village, and we silently set up a firm base.

I had decided that the only way I could get close was to take only a small party. I left Sergeant Beerman, my platoon sergeant, in charge, and as darkness began to set in moved off with Corporal Ambrose (the biggest and strongest man in the platoon), a radio operator, two riflemen and my Ibahn tracker – six of us in all.

Feeling very apprehensive and expecting a platoon of Indonesians or a mine (or both) around every corner, I led this small party towards the kampong, which we could by now both hear and smell.

We reached the perimeter just as it got dark, and settled back into the undergrowth and took it in turns to snatch a few hours' sleep. As dawn came up we were back on the edge of the kampong, watching for signs of military occupation. We didn't have to wait long: a man dressed in jungle green trousers but naked from the waist up came out of a longhouse.

The mine went off

As the kampong came to life it was immediately apparent that there were soldiers there – probably a platoon's-worth. We drew a sketch map, noted everything of even remote military significance, and crept away before the place became fully awake. Sergeant Beerman, undiscovered and unruffled, was waiting for us with the rest of the platoon and we made our getaway as quickly as we could in the direction of the border ridge.

It was while we were trudging up a track in single file along the top of a precipitous jungle-covered knife edge that the mine went off. At first I did not realise what had happened; as I was thrown forward by the force of the explosion I remember thinking, 'Christ, we're being mortared!' – an experience I had had on a previous patrol – but then there was an ominous silence punctuated only by agonised screaming.

It was as if everything was happening in slow

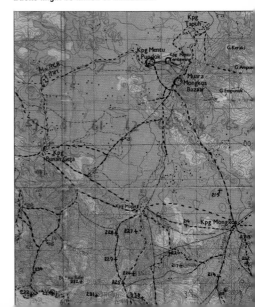

Remote jungle outposts depended entirely on helicopter support. Here a Bristol Type 192 Belvedere brings in a 105-mm light gun/howitzer which is being detached from the rope.

motion. Then, after what seemed like an eternity, I collected my thoughts sufficiently to shout to everybody to get down in all-round defence.

Rifleman Ron Masterman, who had been walking behind me, had trodden on an anti-personnel mine. His left leg had been blown off at the knee. I must have missed the mine by inches. While I organised the platoon, Sergeant Beerman administered morphine and applied a tourniquet to staunch the flow of blood.

The priority was to evacuate Masterman as quickly as we could, otherwise he would die from loss of blood. I went ahead to find a suitable place to chop a hole in the jungle canopy so that a helicopter could winch him out. The others worked like men possessed to chop down several trees; while we worked the Indonesians, who had heard the mine detonate, mortared us – inaccurately, luckily.

When the hole was large enough an RAF Whirlwind helicopter, summoned by radio, appeared and, guided by our smoke grenade, hovered over the hole we had cut. A crewman was lowered 60 metres on a winch and we delivered Ron Masterman to his care. I shall never forget the sight of the stump of his leg disappearing up towards the helicopter. He reached Kuching Military Hospital and recovered; I met him again in 1985.

The map only told part of the story. Most of the ground was covered in dense tropical rain forest. Hacking through the jungle was slow, but the tracks might be mined or ambushed.

Fighting Fit

THE ROYAL MARINES SNIPER COURSE

You awake to Day 25 of the Sniper Training Programme and realise with a jolt that it is the beginning of Badge Test Week!
Throughout the next four days you will be allowed two chances to qualify in the seven skills taught to you during the past weeks. The skills are condensed into six tests:

1 Judging distance
2 Shooting
3 Air photography and map reading
4 Observation
5 Camouflage and concealment
6 Stalking

Each test is broadly similar to those you have done during Course Weeks one to four. The difference now is that any points awarded will be taken into account towards your final assessment. A high pass-mark is essential and everyone feels tense.

Judging distance

Your ability to judge distance accurately is determined by whether you can gauge, to within 10 percent, the range to at least five out of eight objects or features, up to a maximum distance of 1000 metres. Even though you are permitted to use your "optics" – telescopic sight, binoculars and Scout Regiment telescope – it isn't easy. The forty-minute period flies by. The instructor then eases the tension by pointing out the actual distance to each object. The expressions on each face say it all. Grimaces of disgust

Badge Test Week

All the skills you have been learning are put to the test. There are nine different shooting tests, spread over a two-day period of the final week. You fire 60 rounds at targets up to 600 metres away. You need a minimum of 210 points out of 300 to pass this stage.

from those who now know they have only one more chance to pass the test; wide smiles and sighs of relief from those who have been spared the agony of a retrial!

Shooting

There are nine separate types of shoot in the Badge Test, during which a total of 60 rounds are fired from ranges between 300m and 600m at both stationary and moving Figure 11 and Figure 12 targets. Most of the day is spent on the ranges, where your prowess with the L96 is tested to the limit. You are even required to fire wearing NBC gloves and a respirator!

You concentrate as never before. Then, as the results of the initial details are relayed back to the firing

You have to solve six problems in a two-hour session on air photography and mapreading. For many men on the course this is the hardest part of the test and several will have to repeat it.

The observation stand: you need to score at least eight out of 12 to pass this section. The 12 objects are between 10 and 200 metres away; you must spot them and describe them in as much detail as possible.

This time you are on your own: no helpful hints from the instructors. You must convince them that you have the first-class fieldcraft demanded by the sniper's role.

Preparing for the dreaded 'cam and con' exercise on Woodbury Common. Two instructors will observe with binoculars from within 200 metres: your firing position has to be invisible, even with another instructor touching your head.

point, perhaps you begin to relax just a little – but it doesn't pay to become over-confident. You are awarded five points for a "bull" (VSI, or Very Serious Injury); four points for an "inner" (SI, or Serious Injury); and three points for an "outer" (I, or Injured). You are safe only after attaining a minimum total score of 210 points out of a highest possible score

Worried men: the 'cam and con' test is next and the pressure mounts. You have to succeed in the camouflage and concealment phase two out of three times in order to pass.

of 300! You don't need to be an expert in mathematics to work out that only the very best shots have any chance of qualifying, but then most of you *are* marksmen already, having earned the crossed rifles badge during basic training. There is no real reason why you should fail in this test. You know this, you realise you have the ability to do well, and that you probably *will* do very well, but it is still a relief when the day has passed and the final scores come through.

Air Photography and Map Reading

During this two-hour session you are faced with solving six problems. For some this is one of the most difficult of the Badge Tests, for to attain a First Class Pass you must provide four correct answers – five for Sniper Marksman. Each question involves the use of both map and oblique/vertical air photographs. Invariably you will be asked to provide a six-figure grid reference, the range and magnetic

bearing to a number of features, and to plot them onto each photograph.

It is a difficult test and one that will have to be repeated by at least some of the course. After the expiry of the time allowed for each question, an instructor reads out the correct answer so that before long each of you knows just who has passed.

Observation

Twelve objects of a military nature are laid out over an arc of 500 mils between distances of 10m to 200m. You have to name or accurately describe at least eight objects and to plot their positions on a panorama sketch.

The objects in question are partially concealed amongst bushes, trees and in grass, a typical selection consisting of:

1 A nickle-plated whistle
2 Webley .45 revolver
3 Bandolier for 50 rounds (link)
4 Prismatic compass
5 PPSh Sub-machine-gun
6 PPS Sub-machine-gun
7 42 Pattern web sling
8 Armalite bayonet
9 SMG (Sterling) sling
10 Mess tin
11 GPMG gas plug cleaning tool
12 58 Pattern web belt

After forty minutes you hand in your panorama sketch, marked with the objects seen. Most of you are fairly confident of having passed – one or two have managed to identify nearly all of the objects. Or so they think! It comes as a mild shock therefore when one man who had spotted ten objects is awarded only six and a half points – one and a half points less than that required for a pass. He is not told why he has failed, but perhaps he did not plot the objects accurately, or did not provide a satisfactory description? Wherever possible the object has to be described in detail. For example, the .45 Webley revolver is precisely that – and should not therefore be described as simply a Webley! And was the case of the prismatic compass open or shut? All these things must be considered by those repeating the test.

Camouflage and Concealment

You are driven to a spot on Devon's picturesque Woodbury Common and shown an area in which you are to conceal yourselves in a firing position, 150m-250m from two instructors observing from a convenient hilltop. After being granted sufficient time to "cam out" you are allowed six minutes to get into the firing position. The two instructors are then required to move into the area. Each is in radio contact with an observer. As soon as the six minutes are up, the test begins. A "squelch" as a radio relay button is depressed:

"Okay Paul, move within ten."

The instructor walks to within ten metres of a sniper and waits while the observer scans the immediate area for any sign of the hidden man. If he cannot determine the position:

"Get him to fire a shot."

A muffled bang as the sniper squeezes the trigger of his L96. The observer still cannot see anything amiss. He asks the walker to indicate the firing position.

"Okay, move in and touch. . . ."

The stalk. A sniper takes a quick look round during the initial move to the objective. You have two hours to travel 1000 metres, which brings you to within about 250 metres of a pair of observers sitting on a hill.

The instructor places a hand on the head of the sniper and both await the verdict of the observer.

"Hmm, looks good this end. . . ."

If the walker is satisfied that the sniper has chosen his position well, and that the settings on his sight are correct, he will have passed. Now all the sniper has to do is repeat the procedure a second – and a third time if necessary – you need to pass this test two out of three times!

Stalking

As in similar tests conducted previously you must stalk to within 200-250 metres of two observers positioned, as always, on high ground. Separating you from your "target" is 1000 metres of varying countryside that must be negotiated within two hours. A small aerial photograph of the area helps you to decide your route. Initially you are free to move upright, undetected for 200m or so before coming into view of the observers. Then you must use all your stalking skills as you move forward on all fours, and sometimes flat on your belly. The terrain rapidly shifts from fairly solid, gorse-covered ground, to muddy, water-logged swampland and you are quickly soaked to the skin.

You approach a wide dirt track that has to be crossed. It runs along high ground to your left before dipping into a shallow valley. A narrow stream running at right angles to the track has formed a two-foot deep water-hole at the point where the road climbs towards another hill. One man chooses to swim, almost submerged, through the stream. The others crawl quickly across the track at the only spot where it is in "dead ground" in relation to the observers. The rest of the stalk is more straightforward. You choose what you hope is a suitable fire position, check the settings on your sight elevation and deflection drums, aim, and fire. An instructor moves to "within ten". You wait with pounding heart while the observers scan for you with their binoculars.

"Okay. Fire again," you are told.

A wave of relief. Bang. You try to listen to the radio conversation between observer and walker as the latter now indicates your position.

"Touch," requests the observer. The walker moves in and places his hand on your head. A moment of silence as the observer looks directly towards you. A brief, muffled exchange of words. The walker checks your fire position and the settings on your telescopic sight. These must be correct to within one click either way. Then, in order to make sure that you actually have the observers in view, he tells them to make a conspicuous movement. They both wave their hands in the air. The instructor asks what you can see. You tell him.

"Okay. Well done!"

A sniper scurries into the undergrowth after crossing a path. He chose his firing position a short distance further on. The instructors could not spot him, and he was one of the cadre who succeeded in qualifying as a trained sniper.